MEI structured mathematics

Pure Mathematics 4

TERRY HEARD
DAVID MARTIN

Series Editor: Roger Porkess

MEI Structured Mathematics is supported by industry:
BNFL, Casio, GEC, Intercity, JCB, Lucas, The National Grid Company,
Sharp, Texas Instruments, Thorn EMI

Hodder & Stoughton
A MEMBER OF THE HODDER HEADLINE GROUP

Acknowledgements

The illustrations were drawn by Ken Ovington of Precision Art.

The publishers would like to thank University of Cambridge Local Examination Syndicate, the Oxford and Cambridge Examination Board and Schools Maths Project for permission to reproduce past examinations questions in this book. The copyright holders bear no responsibility for the answers to questions taken from past examinations papers which are contained in this publication.

British Library Cataloguing in Publication Data

A catalogue record for this title is held at the British Library.

ISBN 0 340 57861 0

First published 1995
Impression number   10 9 8 7 6 5 4 3 2
Year   1998 1997 1996

Typeset by Multiplex Techniques Ltd.
Printed in Great Britain for Hodder & Stoughton Educational, a division of Hodder Headline PLC, 338 Euston Road, London NW1 3BH by The Bath Press, Bath.

MEI Structured Mathematics

Mathematics is not only a beautiful and exciting subject in its own right but also one that underpins many other branches of learning. It is consequently fundamental to the success of a modern economy.

MEI Structured Mathematics is designed to increase substantially the number of people taking the subject post-GCSE, by making it accessible, interesting and relevant to a wide range of students.

It is a credit accumulation scheme based on 45 hour components which may be taken individually or aggregated to give:

3 Components   AS Mathematics
6 Components   A Level Mathematics
9 Components   A Level Mathematics + AS Further Mathematics
12 Components A Level Mathematics + A Level Further Mathematics

Components may alternatively be combined to give other A or AS certifications (in Statistics, for example) or they may be used to obtain credit towards other types of qualification.

The course is examined by the Oxford and Cambridge Schools Examination Board, with examinations held in January and June each year.

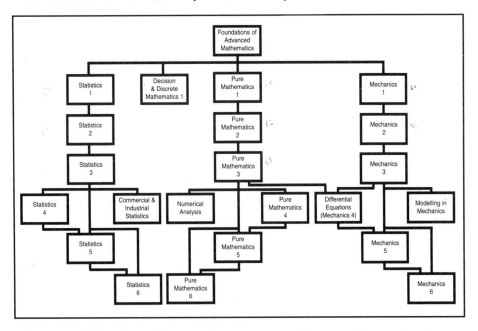

This is one of the series of books written to support the course. Its position within the whole scheme can be seen in the diagram above.

Mathematics in Education and Industry is a curriculum development body which aims to promote the links between Education and Industry in Mathematics, and to produce relevant examination and teaching syllabuses and support material. Since its foundation in the 1960s, MEI has provided syllabuses for GCSE (or previously O Level), Additional Mathematics and A Level.

For more information about MEI Structured Mathematics or other syllabuses and materials, write to MEI Office, 11 Market Street, Bradford-on-Avon BA15 1LL.

Introduction

This is the fourth book in the series covering the pure mathematics of the MEI Structured Mathematics course; you may be using it as the final pure component of an A-level course, or as a continuation into AS or A-level Further Mathematics. In either case, you will have already come across a wide spread of pure mathematics. Two of the chapters here (Graphs and Inequalities, and Vector Geometry) take some of these ideas further; two others (Complex Numbers and Matrices) introduce new topics. The first chapter (Proof), which is rather different in character, is intended to give you an opportunity to deepen your understanding of what mathematics is about, and to look more carefully at the development of mathematical arguments. This is not always easy, but it is worth tackling seriously, since it underpins the whole of the subject.

In writing this book we have been helped by family, friends and colleagues. In particular we are grateful to Mike Jones, Diana Cowey, James Griffin and Roger Porkess for their suggestions. Most influential have been our pupils: their existence has goaded us into getting on with the writing, and their comments (or sometimes confusions) have helped us to improve the drafts. It is a pleasure to record our thanks to them all.

Terry Heard and David Martin

Contents

1 Proof

I have discovered a truly marvellous proof of this, but the margin is too narrow to contain it.

Fermat, 1637

The language of proof

By now you have learnt many mathematical skills, and associated strategies for using them to solve problems. Before moving on to further techniques and methods it is worth pausing to consider again the fundamental idea of *proof* in mathematics. This is important because

- we need careful reasoning to ensure correct conclusions;
- a well constructed proof is an efficient and persuasive way of communicating with others;
- it is often satisfying to sort out the connections between familiar facts and new ones;
- items are easier to remember and use when you can see how they fit together in a logical pattern;
- mathematics without proof is not really mathematics at all!

A reasoned argument begins with certain accepted facts and moves by logical steps to its conclusion. In mathematics a proof is a chain of reasoning which leads in logical steps or *deductions* from a known starting point to a new statement or *theorem*. In other words, a proof has a *starting point* and a *direction*.

At this level the starting point is often taken for granted, but one of the chief motivations for mathematical discovery has been the questioning of basic assumptions: what is accepted at one time (or for one purpose) may well be criticised later for lack of precision. When applying mathematics to solving real problems you will have used the similar process of refining your model by revising its assumptions.

First we shall concentrate on how to show the direction of a proof. A typical step is of the form 'if the statement P is true then it follows that the statement Q is true'

which can be abbreviated to

'if P then Q'   or   'P implies Q'   or symbolically   '$P \Rightarrow Q$'

You should notice that the soundness of the step '$P \Rightarrow Q$' does not depend on whether P is in fact true. For example, the argument

'petrol costs £3 per litre $\Rightarrow$ 10 litres of petrol cost £30'

is valid whatever the actual price of petrol.

The statement '$P \Rightarrow Q$' can also be written as '$Q \Leftarrow P$' ('Q is implied by P'). But you need to be careful not to confuse the statement '$P \Rightarrow Q$' with its *converse* '$P \Leftarrow Q$': these are not saying the same thing, and sometimes the converse of a true statement is false. For example

'Terry was born in the City of London $\Rightarrow$ Terry was born in England'

is true, but the converse

'Terry was born in the City of London $\Leftarrow$ Terry was born in England'

is false.

When '$P \Rightarrow Q$' and '$P \Leftarrow Q$' are both true we say that 'P is equivalent to Q' and write '$P \Leftrightarrow Q$'. The importance of distinguishing between $\Rightarrow$ and $\Leftrightarrow$ is shown in the following example.

EXAMPLE

Solve the equation $x = 6 + \sqrt{x}$.

Solution:

$$x = 6 + \sqrt{x}$$
$$\Leftrightarrow \quad x - 6 = \sqrt{x}$$
$$\Rightarrow \quad (x-6)^2 = x \qquad\qquad ①$$
$$\Leftrightarrow \quad x^2 - 12x + 36 = x$$
$$\Leftrightarrow \quad x^2 - 13x + 36 = 0$$
$$\Leftrightarrow \quad (x-9)(x-4) = 0$$
$$\Leftrightarrow \quad x = 9 \text{ or } x = 4$$

This argument shows that the only possible roots of the original equation are 9 or 4, but since the squaring step ① is not reversible (as shown by using $\Rightarrow$ rather than $\Leftrightarrow$) we must test these possibilities by substitution: since $9 = 6 + \sqrt{9}$ but $4 \neq 6 + \sqrt{4}$ we conclude that 9 is the only root.

Activity

Sketch on the same axes the graphs $y = x - 6$, $y = \sqrt{x}$, $y = -\sqrt{x}$.

Use these to explain the significance of the rejected possibility, $x = 4$.

Vocabulary: necessary, sufficient, if, only if

As alternatives to $\Rightarrow$, $\Leftarrow$ or $\Leftrightarrow$ certain English words can be used in a rather formal way. For example, the fact that every multiple of 6 is also a multiple of 3 can be written as

'n is a multiple of 6' $\Rightarrow$ 'n is a multiple of 3'.

This means that the truth of the statement 'n is a multiple of 6' is enough to ensure the truth of the statement 'n is a multiple of 3'; we say that

'n is a multiple of 6' is a *sufficient condition* for 'n is a multiple of 3'.

The same information can be put another way: n cannot be a multiple of 6 unless n is a multiple of 3, which we express as

'n is a multiple of 6' *only if* 'n is a multiple of 3'.

Similarly the implication

'John has visited France' $\Leftarrow$ 'John has visited Paris'.

means that unless John has visited France he certainly cannot have visited Paris, and we say that

'John has visited France' is a *necessary condition* for 'John has visited Paris'.

or that

'John has visited France' *if* 'John has visited Paris'.

The corresponding phrases which can replace $\Leftrightarrow$ are *necessary and sufficient* or *if and only if*. Sometimes if and only if is shortened to *iff*. All this is summarised in the following table.

$P \Rightarrow Q$	P is a sufficient condition for Q	P only if Q
$P \Leftarrow Q$	P is a necessary condition for Q	P if Q
$P \Leftrightarrow Q$	P is a necessary and sufficient condition for Q	P if and only if Q

Exercise 1A

1. Insert the correct symbol ($\Rightarrow$, $\Leftarrow$ or $\Leftrightarrow$) between these statements.

(a) $\theta = 3\pi/4$ ... $\tan \theta = -1$

(b) $x^2 - 5x + 4 = 0$ ... $x = 4$

(c) $\mathbf{a} . \mathbf{b} = 0$ ... $\mathbf{a}$ is perpendicular to $\mathbf{b}$

(d) $\sqrt{x} = 32$ ... $x^{-\frac{1}{5}} = 0.25$

(e) $y = \sin x$ ... $\dfrac{dy}{dx} = \cos x$

(f) $x^2 < 100$ ... $|x| < 10$

2. Given these statements about a positive integer n

 P: n is a multiple of 3

 Q: n is a multiple of 9

 R: the sum of the digits of n is a multiple of 3

 S: the sum of the digits of n is a multiple of 9

state whether the following statements are correct, and where necessary give a correct version with P, Q, R, S unchanged.

(i) P if Q (ii) Q if P (iii) P if and only if S

(iv) R only if P (v) S only if R (vi) Q if and only if R.

3. For me to have a big breakfast, it is necessary and sufficient that I should not have to go to school. For me to think of a good mathematics question, it is necessary for me to have inspiration. Inspiration comes only if I have a big breakfast. If this is a good mathematics question, what do you conclude?

4. For each of the following say whether the first statement is necessary or sufficient condition for the second (or both or neither).

(a) Jan can swim 1 mile; Jan can swim the English Channel.

(b) I was born in a month containing the letter 'r'; I was not born in May, June, July or August.

(c) ABCD is a rhombus; the diagonals of ABCD bisect each other.

(d) ABCD is a parallelogram; the diagonals of ABCD are perpendicular.

5. State the converse of each of the following theorems, and say whether or not the converse is true.

(a) For a polynomial $P(x)$, if $P(a) = 0$ then $(x - a)$ is a factor of $P(x)$.

(b) If a solid is a prism then the solid has a uniform cross-section.

(c) If triangle ABC has a right angle at A then $a^2 = b^2 + c^2$.

(d) If $y = x^n$ then $\dfrac{dy}{dx} = nx^{n-1}$.

6. The sides of triangle ABC are a, b, c. Say whether each of the following statements is necessary or sufficient (or both or neither) for angle A to be obtuse.

(i) $a > b > c$ (ii) $a > b$ and $a > c$ (iii) $a : b : c = 6 : 4 : 3$ (iv) $a^2 > b^2 + c^2$

7. Show that a decimal which terminates after the nth decimal place can be written in the form of $\dfrac{k}{10^n}$, where k is an integer. Use this to find and prove a necessary and sufficient condition for the fraction $\dfrac{p}{q}$ to have a decimal expansion which terminates.

[**Hint**: Consider the prime factors of q.]

8. Solve the equation $\sqrt{(3x + 1)} = 9 - x$.

9. Solve the equation $\sqrt{(3x)} - \sqrt{(x + 1)} = 1$.

10. Prove that
$$3 - \sqrt{(2x + 3)} = 4 + \sqrt{(x + 1)} \quad \Rightarrow \quad x = -1 \text{ or } 3$$
What are the solutions of $3 - \sqrt{(2x + 3)} = 4 + \sqrt{(x + 1)}$?

Proof in mathematics

The use of proof is one of the special characteristics of mathematics: in other subjects conclusions are based on evidence or opinion, and may have to be rejected or revised in the light of new evidence. So, for example, in physics Einstein's theory of relativity superseded Newton's theory of gravitation, which had been accepted for over 200 years, because relativity can account for observed facts which Newton's theory cannot explain. Both Newton and Einstein used mathematics extensively in their work, but for a physical theory it is the experimental evidence that is crucial, and there is always the possibility that new evidence may call for changes of theory. In mathematics, however, once a theorem is properly proved we can be absolutely sure of its truth.

For Discussion

What does 'proof' mean (a) in criminal law, (b) in civil law? Does proof play a part in medical research, or economics, or weather forecasting?

The central role of proof in mathematics was first recognised by the Greeks, probably as early as 400 BC. About a century later Euclid of Alexandria wrote a geometry and arithmetic text called *The Elements*. For more than two thousand years this was held to be a perfect example of how a body of mathematics could be organised into a logical system: 120 years ago you would probably have been using *The Elements* as one of your textbooks. Here is one of Euclid's classic proofs (Book IX, Proposition 20), preceded by another activity to get you going.

Activity

Let the primes be $p_1, p_2, p_3, \ldots$ in order of size (so that $p_1 = 2, p_2 = 3, p_3 = 5, \ldots$), and let $X_k = p_1 p_2 \ldots p_k + 1$. Work out $X_1, X_2, X_3, \ldots$ until you reach the first X_k which is not prime (or further if you like). Notice that each X_k is either prime or has a prime factor larger than the corresponding p_k.

Theorem

There are infinitely many prime numbers or, in Euclid's words, prime numbers are more than any assigned multitude of prime numbers.

Proof

(1) Suppose there is just a finite number of primes, n say, and let these primes be $p_1, p_2, ..., p_n$.

(2) Form the number $X = p_1 p_2 ... p_n + 1$.

(3) If X is a prime number then it is a prime larger than any of the n primes, so there are more than n primes.

(4) If X is not a prime number then it must be exactly divisible by a prime. But this prime divisor is not p_1 or p_2 or ... or p_n, since when each of these divides X there is remainder 1. Hence there must be some other prime divisor, and so again there are more than n primes.

Options (3) and (4) are the only possibilities, and each of them contradicts (1). Therefore (1) is false, and so there are infinitely many primes.

Proof by contradiction

One powerful general method of showing that a statement P is true is to prove that P cannot be false. To do this we suppose that P is false, and show that this leads to a contradiction. This is illustrated by Euclid's proof above, where P is the statement 'there are infinitely many prime numbers'. Step (1) is to suppose that P is false, then steps (3) and (4) show that this always leads to a contradiction. The conclusion is that P cannot be false, and hence that P must be true.

This method is called *proof by contradiction*; you may also find it described in Latin as *reductio ad absurdum* (reduction to the absurd). Here are two more examples, one a very straightforward preliminary (called a *lemma*), the other of crucial importance in the history of mathematics (see page 55).

Lemma

An even perfect square is the square of an even integer.

Proof

[Notice first exactly what we have to prove: it is very easy to show that the square of an even number is even, since $(2k)^2 = 4k^2$ which is a multiple of 2, but here we want the converse. We have to eliminate the possibility that an even square could arise from squaring an odd number.]

Any odd number can be written in the form $2k + 1$, where k is an integer. The square of this odd number is then

$$(2k + 1)^2 = 4k^2 + 4k + 1 = 2(2k^2 + 2k) + 1$$

which is odd. So if n^2 is even n cannot be odd, so n is even.

Theorem

√2 is irrational (i.e. cannot be written as a fraction).

Proof

Suppose that √2 is not irrational, i.e. that $\sqrt{2} = \dfrac{p}{q}$, where p and q are integers with no common factor (i.e. the fraction $\dfrac{p}{q}$ has been cancelled down to its lowest terms).

$$\sqrt{2} = \frac{p}{q} \implies p^2 = 2q^2 \quad \text{(by definition of √2)} \qquad \text{①}$$

$$\implies p^2 \text{ is even}$$

$$\implies p \text{ is even} \quad \text{(by the Lemma)}$$

$$\implies p = 2r \quad \text{(where } r \text{ is the integer } p/2)$$

$$\implies p^2 = 4r^2$$

$$\implies 2q^2 = 4r^2 \quad \text{(from ①)}$$

$$\implies q^2 = 2r^2$$

$$\implies q^2 \text{ is even}$$

$$\implies q \text{ is even} \quad \text{(by the Lemma again)}$$

$$\implies p \text{ and } q \text{ have the common factor 2.}$$

This contradicts the supposition that √2 could be written as a fraction in its lowest terms. Hence √2 is irrational.

NOTE

Be on your guard against using proof by contradiction unnecessarily. Beginners sometimes produce a proof of a statement P on the following lines:

(1) They suppose P is false.

(2) They then give a direct proof of P.

(3) They note that (2) shows that supposition (1) is false.

(4) They conclude that this proves, by contradiction, that P is true.

Clearly there is no need for (1), (3) or (4) if a direct proof can be found in (2) – but it is not always so easy to spot this when you are involved with the detail. The message is to pay attention to the logical structure of your work as well as getting the details right.

Counter-examples and verifications

In order to prove that a general statement is *not* true all you have to do is to find one particular case for which the statement is false. Such a case is called a *counter-example*. When investigating a statement you may find many cases for which the statement is true, but these *verifications* are not enough to prove the statement, since there may still be a counter-example that you have not yet found. But sometimes a theorem can be proved by verifying *all possible* cases, as in the following example.

Prove that every prime number greater than 3 is of the form $6n \pm 1$, where n is a positive integer. Investigate the converse.

Solution

No integer can be more than 3 away from a multiple of 6, so that every positive integer greater than 3 can be expressed as $6n$ or $6n \pm 1$ or $6n \pm 2$ or $6n + 3$, where n is a positive integer. None of $6n$, $6n \pm 2$ or $6n + 3$ is prime, since these are divisible by 6, 2 or 3 respectively. Therefore every prime greater than 3 is of the form $6n \pm 1$.

The converse states that every number of the form $6n \pm 1$ is a prime greater than 3. This is false, as shown by the counter-example $6 \times 4 + 1 = 25$, which is not prime.

HISTORICAL NOTE

One famous counter-example took 100 years to find. In 1640 the French lawyer and great mathematician Pierre de Fermat claimed that the numbers $F_n = 2^{2^n} + 1$ are prime for all integers $n \geqslant 0$. He knew that the first five numbers, 3 ,5 ,17,257, 65 537, are all prime, and he had failed after extensive searching to find any factor of the next, $F_5 = 2^{2^5} + 1 = 4\,294\,967\,297$. He wrote: 'I do not have an exact proof, but I have excluded such a large quantity of divisors by infallible proofs, and I have such great insights (lumières) which establish my thought that I should be sorry to retract'. But despite his confidence Fermat was wrong, though it was not until 1739 that an even greater mathematician, Leonhard Euler (1707 – 83), discovered that F_5 is divisible by 641.

Exercise 1B

1. Prove that a perfect square which is a multiple of 3 is the square of a multiple of 3.

2. Prove that $\sqrt{3}$ is irrational.

3. Give either a proof or a counter-example for each of the following statements about positive numbers.

   (i)   Rational + irrational = irrational.

   (ii) Irrational + irrational = irrational.

   (iii) Rational $\times$ irrational = irrational.

   (iv) Irrational $\times$ irrational = irrational.

4. (i) Prove that the angle subtended at the centre of a circle by an arc is twice the angle subtended at a point on the rest of the circumference by the same arc (i.e. $\angle AOC = 2\angle ABC$ in left-hand diagram).

   (ii) Prove that the opposite angles of a cyclic quadrilateral are supplementary (i.e. $\angle ABC + \angle ADC = 180°$ in right-hand diagram).

   (iii) Prove the converse of the theorem in part (ii)
   (i.e. $\angle ABC + \angle ADC = 180° \Rightarrow ABCD$ is cyclic).

 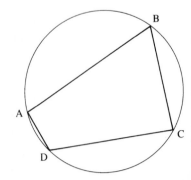

[**Hint** for part (iii): Suppose not, so that D is not on the circumcircle of triangle ABC; let AD meet this circle at E; obtain a contradiction by using part (ii) with ABCE.]

5. Each one of a finite number of points along a straight line is coloured either red or blue. The line segment between adjacent coloured points is coloured green if the end points of the segment are the same colour, or yellow if they are different colours. Prove that if the first and last points along the line are different colours then the number of yellow segments is odd.

6. (i) Six points are chosen in space, and each possible pair of these points is joined by a line segment. Each line segment is coloured either green or yellow. Prove that there is at least one monochrome (all green or all yellow) triangle formed by these segments.

   (ii) Investigate whether part (i) is true when there are five points instead of six. Justify your conclusion.

7. Prove that if p is a prime greater than 3 then $p^2 - 1$ is a multiple of 24.

   [**Hint**: Use the example on page 9.]

8. (i) By considering all the possible units digits of the positive integer n, prove that $n^5 - n$ is always divisible by 10.

   (ii) By factorising $n^5 - n$, prove that $n^5 - n$ is always divisible by 30.

9. Integers of the form $4k + 1$ are called type A; those of the form $4k - 1$ are called type B.

   (i) Prove that every odd integer is either of type A or of type B.

   (ii) Prove that the product of two type A integers is itself of type A.

   Complete these statements:

   $$\text{type A} \times \text{type B} = \text{type ?}$$

   $$\text{type B} \times \text{type B} = \text{type ?}$$

   (iii) Prove that any integer of type B must have an odd number of factors of type B.

   (iv) List three primes of type A and three primes of type B.

   (v) Adapt Euclid's proof of the Theorem on page 7 to prove that there are infinitely many primes of type B.

   [**Hint**: let $Y = 4q_1q_2 \ldots q_n - 1$, where $q_1, q_2, \ldots, q_n$ are primes of type B.]

   (vi) Explain why a similar method fails to prove that there infinitely many primes of type A. Does it follow that there is only a finite number of such primes?

10. (i) Prove that the sum of two or more consecutive positive integers must have an odd factor greater than 1.

    (ii) Deduce that numbers of the form 2^n cannot be the sum of two or more consecutive positive integers.

    (iii) Investigate which integers are the sum of two or more consecutive positive integers, and prove your conjectures.

Induction in mathematics

Activity

Work out the first four terms of this pattern:

$$1^2 =$$

$$1^2 - 2^2 + 3^2 =$$

$$1^2 - 2^2 + 3^2 - 4^2 + 5^2 =$$

... ...

Look carefully at your answers (in particular their factors), and *predict* the next two terms. Then check your predictions.

Activity

Work out the value of

$$1 + {}^nC_2 + {}^nC_4$$

for $n = 1, 2, 3, 4$. Look carefully at your answers, and *predict* the values for $n = 5, 6$. Then check your predictions.

(Reminder: ${}^nC_r = \dfrac{n!}{r!(n-r)!}$ for $n \geqslant r$, and ${}^nC_r = 0$ for $n < r$.)

It is not possible to prove something until you know what you want to prove: the systematic organisation comes *after* the result is known. Mathematical discovery does not usually come by logical deduction; new truths are more often found by experiment with particular examples, by analogy, by intuition, or just 'out of the blue' (though inspiration is unlikely to come without a good deal of hard work to prepare the ground).

The two activities you have just done illustrate one common way of making progress in mathematics. The examination of a number of particular cases suggests a pattern, which can usually be put into algebra to form a *conjecture* (i.e. a guess) about a more general result. This investigative process is called *induction*.

The conjecture can then be tested in further particular cases. If you find a counter-example (a case where the conjecture is not true) then the conjecture is definitely disproved. For example, if in the last activity you made the obvious prediction $1 + {}^nC_2 + {}^nC_4 = 2^{n-1}$ you will have found that $n = 6$ gives a counter-example, so the conjecture is wrong.

If, on the other hand, the further particular cases agree with the conjecture you may well feel that you are on the right line, but you can never be certain that further trial might not reveal a counter-example: the conjecture has been confirmed, but not proved.

To illustrate how we can get beyond this stage, we look more closely at the activity on page 11. This involves the alternating sum of an odd number of squares. If there are $(2n - 1)$ squares this sum is

$$1^2 - 2^2 + 3^2 - 4^2 + 5^2 - \ldots - (2n - 2)^2 + (2n - 1)^2$$

This activity has shown that the conjecture

$$1^2 - 2^2 + 3^2 - 4^2 + 5^2 - \ldots - (2n - 2)^2 + (2n - 1)^2 = n(2n - 1) \qquad \text{(C)}$$

is true for $n = 1, 2, \ldots, 6$. We call this conjecture (C), and we want to prove that it is true for *all* positive integers n. It is not easy to see how to do this by deduction from known results, so we use a different approach.

If (C) is true for a particular integer, $n = k$ say, then

$$1^2 - 2^2 + 3^2 - 4^2 + 5^2 - \ldots - (2k - 2)^2 + (2k - 1)^2 = k(2k - 1)$$

Subtracting the next square and adding the one after that gives

$$1^2 - 2^2 + 3^2 - 4^2 + 5^2 - \ldots - (2k-2)^2 + (2k-1)^2 - (2k)^2 + (2k+1)^2$$

$$= k(2k-1) - (2k)^2 + (2k+1)^2$$

If (C) is also true for the next integer, $n = k + 1$, then this right-hand side should equal

$$(k+1)(2(k+1)-1) = (k+1)(2k+1)$$

so the next task is to show that this is correct:

$$k(2k-1) - (2k)^2 + (2k+1)^2 = 2k^2 - k - 4k^2 + 4k^2 + 4k + 1$$

$$= 2k^2 + 3k + 1$$

$$= (k+1)(2k+1)$$

as we wanted.

Since (C) is true when $n = 6$ it follows (taking $k = 6$) that (C) is true when $n = 7$; hence (taking $k = 7$) (C) is true when $n = 8$, and so on. By stepping on like this we can reach any positive integer n however great, so we have proved that (C) is true for *every* positive integer.

This form of proof can be compared with the process of climbing a ladder: if we can (1) reach the bottom rung and (2) get from one rung to the next, then we can climb as far as we like up the ladder (figure 1.1).

Figure 1.1

The corresponding stages in the proof are

(1) showing that (C) is true for $n = 1$ (though in fact you checked it up to $n = 6$);

(2) showing that if (C) is true for any particular value of n, $n = k$ say, then it is true for the next value, $n = k + 1$.

This method of proof is called *proof by mathematical induction* (or just *proof by induction*). The word induction is used here because this is a powerful way to prove many of the conjectures which can be found by the sort of inductive investigation which started this section. Here is a more formal statement of the method, plus some more examples.

Proof by mathematical induction

The method of proof by induction can be summarised as follows.

A conjecture (C) involving the positive integer n is true for all n provided that

(1) (C) is true when $n = 1$

and (2) if (C) is true when $n = k$, then (C) is true when $n = k + 1$.

Both these statements must be proved; since (1) is usually a simple verification, whereas (2) can be quite complicated, there is a danger that you will concentrate on (2) and forget about (1) – but it is no use being able to climb the ladder if you cannot reach the bottom rung!

Activity

1. Let (C) be the conjecture

$$2 + 4 + 6 + \dots + 2n = (n + \tfrac{1}{2})^2$$

Prove that if (C) is true when $n = k$ then (C) is true when $n = k + 1$.

Explain why (C) is not true for any positive integer n.

2. Find a conjecture for which statement (1) is true, but (2) is not.

EXAMPLE

Prove that for all positive integers n

$$1^2 + 2^2 + 3^2 + \dots + n^2 = \tfrac{1}{6} n(n + 1)(2n + 1)$$ (C)

Solution

(1) The statement (C) is true when $n = 1$, since $1^2 = \tfrac{1}{6} . 1. 2. 3$.

(2) If (C) is true when $n = k$, that is if

$$1^2 + 2^2 + 3^2 + \dots + k^2 = \tfrac{1}{6} k(k + 1)(2k + 1)$$

Target: $\tfrac{1}{6}(k + 1)(k + 2)(2k + 3$

$$\begin{aligned}
\text{then } 1^2 + 2^2 + 3^2 + \dots + k^2 + (k + 1)^2 &= \tfrac{1}{6} k(k + 1)(2k + 1) + (k + 1)^2 \\
&= (k + 1)[\tfrac{1}{6} k(2k + 1) + k + 1] \\
&= \tfrac{1}{6}(k + 1)[k(2k + 1) + 6k + 6] \\
&= \tfrac{1}{6}(k + 1)(2k^2 + 7k + 6) \\
&= \tfrac{1}{6}(k + 1)(k + 2)(2k + 3)
\end{aligned}$$

so that (C) is true when $n = k + 1$.

From (1) and (2) by induction (C) is true for all $n \geqslant 1$.

NOTE

In the rather complicated manipulation in part (2) of this proof we have to reach the right-hand side of (C) with n replaced by k + 1. It is worth making a note of this target before starting the heavy algebra, to guide the working: for example, in this case, the target shows that it is a good idea to keep $\frac{1}{6}(k + 1)$ as a factor and then sort out the rest of the expression.

EXAMPLE

Prove that $y = x^n \Rightarrow \dfrac{dy}{dx} = nx^{n-1}$ for all integers $n \geqslant 1$.   (C)

Solution

(1)   (C) is true when $n = 1$ since $y = x \Rightarrow \dfrac{dy}{dx} = 1 = 1x^0$.

(2)   By writing x^{k+1} as $x \times x^k$ and using the method of differentiating a product we have

$$y = x^{k+1} \Rightarrow \frac{dy}{dx} = x \times \frac{d}{dx}(x^k) + 1 \times x^k$$

So if (C) is true when $n = k$ then

$$y = x^{k+1} \Rightarrow \frac{dy}{dx} = x \times kx^{k-1} + 1 \times x^k \quad \text{Target: } (k+1)x^k$$

$$= kx^k + x^k$$

$$= (k+1)\, x^k$$

and therefore (C) is true when $n = k + 1$.

From (1) and (2) by induction (C) is true for all $n \geqslant 1$.

EXAMPLE

Prove that $u_n = 4^n + 6n - 1$ is divisible by 9 for all $n \geqslant 1$.   (C)

Solution

(1) $u_1 = 4 + 6 - 1 = 9$,   so (C) is true when $n = 1$.

(2)   We want to show that u_k is divisible by $9 \Rightarrow u_{k+1}$ is divisible by 9.

Now $u_{k+1} = 4^{k+1} + 6(k + 1) - 1 = 4 \times 4^k + 6k + 5$

$$= 4(4^k + 6k - 1) - 18k + 9 \quad \text{Introducing } u_k \text{ and then compensating}$$

$$= 4u_k - 9(2k - 1).$$

Therefore if u_k is a multiple of 9 then so is u_{k+1}.

From (1) and (2) by induction (C) is true for all $n \geqslant 1$.

Sometimes the method of mathematical induction has to be modified, as illustrated in the next two examples.

EXAMPLE The sequence of numbers $u_1, u_2, u_3, \ldots$ is defined by

$$u_1 = 1, \ u_2 = 7, \ u_{n+2} = 7u_{n+1} - 12u_n \quad (n \geqslant 1)$$

Prove that $u_n = 4^n - 3^n$.

Solution

(1) Since u_{n+2} depends on the *two* preceding terms of the sequence, we have to show that (C) is true for the first two values of n. When $n = 1$, $4^n - 3^n = 4 - 3 = 1$, and when $n = 2$, $4^n - 3^n = 16 - 9 = 7$, so (C) is true when $n = 1$ and 2.

(2) If (C) is true when $n = k$ *and* when $n = k + 1$ then

$$
\begin{aligned}
u_{k+2} &= 7(4^{k+1} - 3^{k+1}) - 12(4^k - 3^k) \\
&= 7 \times 4^{k+1} - 3 \times 4^{k+1} - 7 \times 3^{k+1} + 4 \times 3^{k+1} \\
&= (7 - 3)4^{k+1} - (7 - 4)3^{k+1} \\
&= 4^{k+2} - 3^{k+2}
\end{aligned}
$$

so that (C) is true when $n = k + 2$.

Thus if (C) is true for any two consecutive values of n then it is also true for the next value of n. But (C) is true for the consecutive values $n = 1, 2$. Hence by induction (C) is true for all $n \geqslant 1$.

EXAMPLE Find the set of positive integers n for which $2^n > n^2$.

Solution

The first few values of n give the following

n	1	2	3	4	5	6
2^n	2	4	8	16	32	64
n^2	1	4	9	16	25	36
$2^n > n^2$?	Yes	No	No	No	Yes	Yes

This suggests that the statement $2^n > n^2$, which we call (C), is true for $n = 1$ and for $n \geqslant 5$.

To prove this, suppose that (C) is true when $n = k$, where $k \geqslant 5$. Then

$$2^k > k^2 \Rightarrow 2^{k+1} > 2k^2 \quad \text{(multiplying by 2)}$$

$$
\begin{aligned}
&= k^2 + k^2 \\
&\geqslant k^2 + 5k \quad \text{(since } k \geqslant 5) \\
&> k^2 + 2k + 1 \\
&= (k + 1)^2
\end{aligned}
$$

Target:
$$2^{k+1} > (k + 1)^2$$

so that (C) is true when $n = k + 1$. Hence by induction (C) is true for all $n \geqslant 5$ (and also, as the table shows, for $n = 1$).

NOTE

In this example the mathematical induction starts at $n = 5$ instead of the usual $n = 1$. The statement is true when $n = 1$, but the essential step of showing that $2^k > k^2 \Rightarrow 2^{k+1} > (k+1)^2$ does not work until $k \geqslant 3$, and (C) is not true again until $n = 5$.

Exercise 1C

In Questions 1 – 8, by considering the first few values of n, suggest a general formula for u_n, and prove your conjecture by mathematical induction.

1. $u_n = 1 + 3 + 5 + \dots + (2n - 1)$.   (This was the first example of proof by induction ever published, by Francesco Maurolycus in 1575.)

2. $u_n = 4 + 7 + 10 + \dots + (3n + 1)$

3. $u_n = \dfrac{1}{1 \times 2} + \dfrac{1}{2 \times 3} + \dfrac{1}{3 \times 4} + \dots + \dfrac{1}{n(n+1)}$

4. $u_n = \dfrac{1}{3} + \dfrac{1}{15} + \dfrac{1}{35} + \dots + \dfrac{1}{4n^2 - 1}$

5. $u_n = 1 \times 1! + 2 \times 2! + 3 \times 3! + \dots + n \times n!$

6. $u_n = \left(1 - \dfrac{1}{2^2}\right)\left(1 - \dfrac{1}{3^2}\right)\left(1 - \dfrac{1}{4^2}\right) \dots \left(1 - \dfrac{1}{n^2}\right)$

7. $u_{n+1} = \dfrac{u_n}{u_n + 1}, u_1 = 1$

8. $u_{n+1} = 3u_n + 2, u_1 = 2$

9. Prove by induction that $1^3 + 2^3 + 3^3 + \dots + n^3 = \frac{1}{4}n^2(n+1)^2$.

10. Prove by induction that $1 + x + x^2 + \dots + x^{n-1} = \dfrac{1 - x^n}{1 - x}$ $(x \neq 1)$.

11. Prove that
$$\cos \theta \cos 2\theta \cos 4\theta \dots \cos 2^n \theta = \dfrac{\sin 2^{n+1}\theta}{2^{n+1} \sin \theta}$$
provided that $\sin \theta \neq 0$.

12. Find the smallest integer N for which $3^n < n!$. Prove that $3^n < n!$ for all $n \geqslant N$.

13. Find, with proof, the set of positive integers n for which $2^n > n^3$.

14. (i) Let r_n be the number of sections into which an infinite straight line is divided by n distinct points marked on it. Find a formula for r_n.

Exercise 1C continued

    (ii) Let s_n be the number of regions into which a plane is divided by n distinct lines, of which no two are parallel and no three concurrent. Prove by induction that $s_n = \frac{1}{2}n(n + 1) + 1$.

    (iii) Let t_n be the number of regions into which space is divided by n distinct planes, of which no two are parallel, no three meet in a line, and no four meet in a point. Explain why $t_{n+1} = t_n + s_n$. Find a formula for t_n, and prove it by induction.

15. Examine the divisors of $11^n + 3 \times 4^{n-1}$ for $n = 1, 2, 3, 4$. Form a conjecture based on this evidence, and prove it by induction.

16. Prove that $11^{n+2} + 12^{2n+1}$ is divisible by 133 for $n \geqslant 0$.

17. Given that $u_{n+1} = 4u_n - 6$, find, with proof, an expression for u_n
(i) when $u_1 = 2$; (ii) when $u_1 = 3$.

18. Given that $u_{n+2} = 10u_{n+1} - 25u_n$ with $u_1 = 0$ and $u_2 = 1$, prove that $u_n = (n-1)5^{n-2}$.

19. Given that $u_{n+2} = 6u_{n+1} - 4u_n$ with $u_1 = 6$ and $u_2 = 28$, prove that $u_n = (3 + \sqrt{5})^n + (3 - \sqrt{5})^n$.

Deduce that, for $n > 1$, the integer nearest to $(3 + \sqrt{5})^n$ is divisible by 2^n.

20. The *Fibonacci numbers* $1, 1, 2, 3, 5, 8, 13, \ldots$ are defined by

$$f_{n+2} = f_{n+1} + f_n \quad \text{with} \quad f_1 = f_2 = 1$$

They are named after Leonardo of Pisa (c. 1170 – 1250), who was also known as Fibonacci (son of Bonacci) and, ironically, Leonard the Blockhead. He is credited with the introduction of Arabic numerals to Europe from Morocco where he was educated.

(i) Find and prove a rule for determining whether f_n is odd or even.

(ii) Investigate how the sum of the first n Fibonacci numbers is related to one of the later Fibonacci numbers. Do likewise for the alternate sums

$$f_1 + f_3 + f_5 + \ldots \quad \text{and} \quad f_2 + f_4 + f_6 + \ldots .$$

(iii) Prove that $f_n f_{n+2} - f_{n+1}^2 = (-1)^{n+1}$, and investigate $f_n f_{n+3} - f_{n+1} f_{n+2}$.

(iv) Prove that $f_n = (\alpha^n - \beta^n)/\sqrt{5}$, where $\alpha = (1 + \sqrt{5})/2$ and $\beta = (1 - \sqrt{5})/2$.

(v) Deduce from part (iv) that $f_{n+1}/f_n \to \alpha$ as $n \to \infty$.

(vi) [For those who like a challenge!] Prove that

$$f_{n+m+1} = f_n f_m + f_{n+1} f_{m+1}$$

Deduce that if m divides n, then f_m divides f_n.

21. Comment on the following 'proof' of the 'theorem':

'In every examination all candidates get the same number of marks'   (T)

Proof by induction on n, the number of candidates.

(1) When $n = 1$ there is only one candidate, so (T) is true.

(2) Suppose (T) is true when $n = k$. Consider an examination with $k + 1$ candidates $A, B, C, D, \ldots$. The k candidates $B, C, D, \ldots$ have the same mark, since (T) is true when $n = k$. Therefore B and C have the same mark. The k candidates $A, C, D, \ldots$ also have the same mark, so A and C have the same mark. Therefore $A, B, C, D, \ldots$ all have the same mark, and (T) is true when $n = k + 1$. From (1) and (2) by induction (T) is true for all $n \geqslant 1$.

Summation of finite series

The sum S_n of a finite series is found by adding together the first n terms of a finite sequence. If the rth term of the sequence is u_r then

$$S_n = u_1 + u_2 + \ldots + u_n = \sum_{r=1}^{n} u_r$$

In earlier components you have already met these important examples:

Arithmetic series: $\quad u_r = a + (r-1)d \qquad S_n = \tfrac{1}{2}n\,[2a + (n-1)d]$

Geometric series: $\quad u_r = ax^{r-1} \qquad\quad S_n = a(1-x^n)/(1-x)$

Binomial series: $\quad u_r = {}^nC_r x^r \qquad\quad S_n = (1+x)^n - 1$

Note that the binomial expansion of $(1 + x)^n$ has $n + 1$ terms, starting with $u_0 = 1$; this has to be subtracted to give S_n.

As you have seen in the previous section, if you can guess what the sum of a series is you can often prove it by mathematical induction. Now we look at some other ways of dealing with finite sums. Some of these results will be familiar to you; the important thing is to concentrate on the methods of obtaining them.

EXAMPLE

Find $\displaystyle\sum_{r=1}^{n} r$.

Solution

The series is just the sum of the first n positive integers, which can be found easily as the sum of an arithmetic series. But as an alternative we can use the ancient Greek idea of triangle numbers. The nth triangle number, T_n, is the number of dots in a triangular array having n rows, with 1 dot on the top row, 2 dots on the second row, 3 dots on the third row, and so on (see diagram on right).

So the sum we want is simply T_n. But the triangle for T_n can be put next to a congruent inverted triangle to form a rectangle with n rows and $(n + 1)$ columns as shown below for the case $n = 5$.

The number of dots in this rectangle is $n(n + 1)$, so that $T_n = \sum_{r=1}^{n} r = \frac{1}{2}n(n+1)$.

EXAMPLE

Find $\sum_{r=1}^{n} r^2$.

Solution

The formula has already been proved by induction in the example on page 14. Here we use a more direct method which does not depend upon knowing the answer. This starts by noting that

$$(2r + 1)^3 - (2r - 1)^3 \equiv 8r^3 + 12r^2 + 6r + 1 - (8r^3 - 12r^2 + 6r - 1) \equiv 24r^2 + 2$$

Swapping the right and left-hand sides and substituting $r = 1, 2, 3, ..., n$ successively gives

$$24 \times 1^2 + 2 = 3^3 - 1^3$$
$$24 \times 2^2 + 2 = 5^3 - 3^3$$
$$24 \times 3^2 + 2 = 7^3 - 5^3$$
$$... \quad ... \quad ... \quad ...$$
$$24 \times n^2 + 2 = (2n + 1)^3 - (2n - 1)^3$$

When these n equations are added together all except two of the cubes on the right-hand side cancel, giving

$$24 \sum_{r=1}^{n} r^2 + 2n = (2n + 1)^3 - 1^3$$

$$\Rightarrow \quad 24 \sum_{r=1}^{n} r^2 = 8n^3 + 12n^2 + 6n + 1 - 1 - 2n$$

$$= 8n^3 + 12n^2 + 4n$$

$$= 4n(2n^2 + 3n + 1)$$

$$= 4n(n + 1)(2n + 1)$$

$$\Rightarrow \quad \sum_{r=1}^{n} r^2 = \frac{1}{6}n(n + 1)(2n + 1)$$

This example illustrates a useful method for summing series, called the *method of differences*. The idea is to express each term u_r of the sum as the difference of consecutive terms of another sequence, i e. to find v_r such that

$$u_r = v_r - v_{r-1} \quad \text{for} \quad r = 1, 2, 3, \dots, n$$

Then
$$\sum_{r=1}^{n} u_r = (v_1 - v_0) + (v_2 - v_1) + (v_3 - v_2) + \dots + (v_n - v_{n-1})$$

On the right-hand side all but two of the v_r cancel, leaving only $v_n - v_0$.

Therefore
$$\sum_{r=1}^{n} u_r = v_n - v_0.$$

The cancelling of nearly all the v_r is similar to the way in which the interior sections of a collapsible telescope disappear when it is compressed, so this can be described as a *telescoping a sum*.

Activities

1. Prove formally by induction that if $u_r = v_r - v_{r-1}$ for $r = 1, 2, 3, \dots, n$ then

$$\sum_{r=1}^{n} u_r = v_n - v_0$$

2. What v_r was used in the solution of the example on page 20?

3. By taking $v_r = r(r+1)(r+2)$ and using the method of differences, find $\displaystyle\sum_{r=1}^{n} r(r+1)$.

EXAMPLE

Find $\displaystyle\sum_{r=1}^{n} \frac{1}{r(r+1)}$.

Solution

By partial fractions
$$\frac{1}{r(r+1)} = \frac{1}{r} - \frac{1}{r+1}$$

so
$$\sum_{r=1}^{n} \frac{1}{r(r+1)} = \left(1 - \frac{1}{2}\right) + \left(\frac{1}{2} - \frac{1}{3}\right) + \left(\frac{1}{3} - \frac{1}{4}\right) + \dots + \left(\frac{1}{n} - \frac{1}{n+1}\right)$$

$$= 1 - \frac{1}{n+1} = \frac{n}{n+1}$$

Note that this uses the method of differences with $v_r = -1/(r+1)$.

The next example uses a rather more complicated telescoping sum.

EXAMPLE

Find $\displaystyle\sum_{r=1}^{n} \frac{r+4}{r(r+1)(r+2)}$.

Solution

By partial fractions $\dfrac{r+4}{r(r+1)(r+2)} = \dfrac{2}{r} - \dfrac{3}{r+1} + \dfrac{1}{r+2}$, so

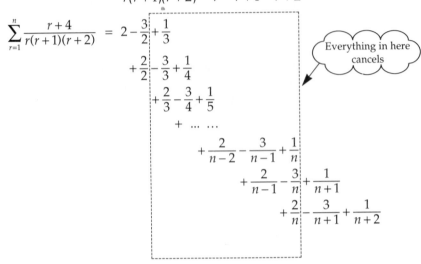

Everything in here cancels

$$\sum_{r=1}^{n} \frac{r+4}{r(r+1)(r+2)} = 2 - \frac{3}{2} + \frac{1}{3}$$
$$+ \frac{2}{2} - \frac{3}{3} + \frac{1}{4}$$
$$+ \frac{2}{3} - \frac{3}{4} + \frac{1}{5}$$
$$+ \; ... \; ...$$
$$+ \frac{2}{n-2} - \frac{3}{n-1} + \frac{1}{n}$$
$$+ \frac{2}{n-1} - \frac{3}{n} + \frac{1}{n+1}$$
$$+ \frac{2}{n} - \frac{3}{n+1} + \frac{1}{n+2}$$

Most of the terms cancel, leaving

$$\sum_{r=1}^{n} \frac{r+4}{r(r+1)(r+2)} = 2 - \frac{3}{2} + \frac{2}{2} + \frac{1}{n+1} - \frac{3}{n+1} + \frac{1}{n+2}$$
$$= \frac{3}{2} - \frac{2}{n+1} + \frac{1}{n+2}$$

In Question 9 of Exercise 1C (page 17) you proved that $\displaystyle\sum_{r=1}^{n} r^3 = \frac{1}{4} n^2 (n+1)^2$,

and the example on page 19 shows that $\displaystyle\sum_{r=1}^{n} r = \frac{1}{2} n(n+1)$. It follows that

$$\sum_{r=1}^{n} r^3 = \left(\sum_{r=1}^{n} r \right)^2$$

This is really just a curiosity, though it does make it easy to remember the formula for the sum of cubes. The following geometrical proof of the same result may appeal to you.

Since $r^3 = r \times r^2$, we represent the cube r^3 not as a volume but as the area of r squares of side r, so that the sum of cubes is the total area of

1 square of side 1 + 2 squares of side 2 + 3 squares of side 3 + ...
+ n squares of side n

These can be arranged as shown (for $n = 5$, but the pattern continues) in figure 1.2.

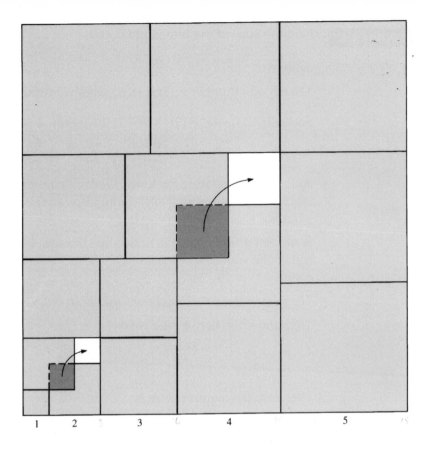

Figure 1.2

The even-sided squares overlap, but there is a gap (unshaded) of exactly the same size as the overlap, so the overlapping regions can be moved to fill the gaps. Therefore the squares exactly fill a large square, whose side is $(1 + 2 + 3 + ... + n)$, which is what we set out to prove.

The three important results

$$\sum_{r=1}^{n} r = \tfrac{1}{2}n(n+1) \qquad \sum_{r=1}^{n} r^2 = \tfrac{1}{6}n(n+1)(2n+1) \qquad \sum_{r=1}^{n} r^3 = \tfrac{1}{4}n^2(n+1)^2$$

can be used to sum further series, as in the following examples.

EXAMPLE

Find $\displaystyle\sum_{r=1}^{n} r(r+2)$.

Solution

$$\sum_{r=1}^{n} r(r+2) = \sum_{r=1}^{n} \left(r^2 + 2r\right) = \sum_{r=1}^{n} r^2 + 2\sum_{r=1}^{n} r$$

$$= \tfrac{1}{6}n(n+1)(2n+1) + 2 \times \tfrac{1}{2}n(n+1)$$

$$= \tfrac{1}{6}n(n+1)(2n+1+6)$$

$$= \tfrac{1}{6}n(n+1)(2n+7)$$

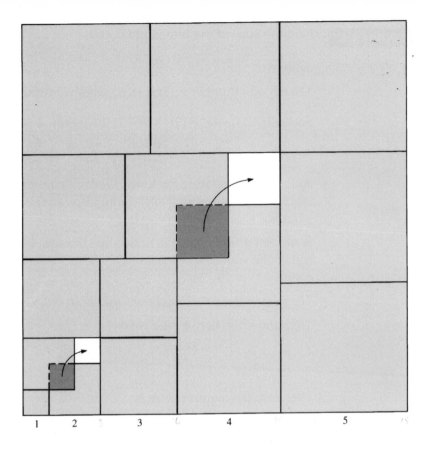

EXAMPLE

Find the sum of the first n odd cubes.

Solution

The rth odd number is $(2r - 1)$, so what we want is $\displaystyle\sum_{r=1}^{n} (2r - 1)^3$.

Since $(2r - 1)^3 = 8r^3 - 12r^2 + 6r - 1$, the required sum equals

$$8 \sum_{r=1}^{n} r^3 - 12 \sum_{r=1}^{n} r^2 + 6 \sum_{r=1}^{n} r - n$$

and we can substitute the known formula for each of the three sums involved and simplify. This is straightforward, though the algebra is rather tedious.

A simpler alternative is to notice that the sum of the first n odd cubes equals the sum of the first $2n$ cubes minus the sum of the first n even cubes.

The sum of the first $2n$ cubes is $\frac{1}{4}(2n)^2(2n+1)^2 = n^2(2n+1)^2$.

The sum of the first n even cubes is

$$2^3 + 4^3 + 6^3 + ... + (2n)^3 = 8(1^3 + 2^3 + 3^3 + ... + n^3)$$
$$= 2n^2(n + 1)^2$$

Therefore the required sum is

$$n^2(2n + 1)^2 - 2n^2(n + 1)^2 = n^2[(2n + 1)^2 - 2(n + 1)^2]$$
$$= n^2(2n^2 - 1)$$

Exercise 1D

Throughout this exercise S_k is used as an abbreviation for $\displaystyle\sum_{r=1}^{n} r^k$.

In Questions 1 – 4, find $\displaystyle\sum_{r=1}^{n} u_r$, where u_r is the given expression.

1. $2r - 1$　　　**2.** $r(3r + 1)$　　　**3.** $(r + 1)r^2$　　　**4.** $4r^3 - 6r^2 + 4r - 1$

5. Find $\displaystyle\sum_{r=1}^{n} (r + 4)^3$

    (i)　by expanding $(r + 4)^3$ and using S_1, S_2 and S_3;

    (ii)　by substituting $s = r + 4$.

6. Find $1^3 + 2^3 + 4^3 + 5^3 + 7^3 + 8^3 + ... + (3n - 2)^3 + (3n - 1)^3$.

7. On a fruit stall a pile of oranges is arranged to form a truncated square pyramid. Each layer is a square, with the lengths of side of successive layers reducing by one orange. The bottom layer measures $2n \times 2n$ oranges, and there are n layers.

Prove that the number of oranges used is $\frac{1}{6} n(2n + 1)(7n + 1)$. What is the greatest n which uses fewer than 1000 oranges?

8. Cannonballs at a military museum are to be displayed in pyramidal piles. Prove that a triangular pyramid in which each side of the base contains $2n$ cannonballs can be rearranged to give exactly four square pyramids in which each side of the base contains n cannonballs. (In both cases the lengths of side of successive layers reduce by one cannonball.)

9. Prove that every cube can be expressed as the difference of two squares. Find integers p and q such that $p^2 - q^2 = 57^3$.

In Questions 10 – 13, use the method of differences to find $\sum_{r=1}^{n} u_r$ for the given u_r.

10. $\dfrac{1}{r(r+2)}$ **11.** $\dfrac{r}{(r+2)(r+3)(r+4)}$ **12.** $\dfrac{1}{r(r+1)(r+2)}$ **13.** $\dfrac{2r+1}{r^2(r+1)^2}$

14. Use the method of differences with $v_r = r^2(r+1)^2$ to prove the formula for S_3.

15. (i) Use the method of differences with $v_r = r(r+1)(r+2)(r+3)$ to find
$$\sum_{r=1}^{n} r(r+1)(r+2).$$

(ii) From the formulae for $\sum_{r=1}^{n} r$, $\sum_{r=1}^{n} r(r+1)$ and $\sum_{r=1}^{n} r(r+1)(r+2)$ make a

conjecture about $\sum_{r=1}^{n} r(r+1)(r+2) \dots (r+k)$ and prove it.

16. Using the idea suggested in the diagram, or otherwise, prove that
$$1 \times n + 2(n-1) + 3(n-2) + \dots + n \times 1 = \tfrac{1}{6}n(n+1)(n+2)$$

17. Use the method of differences to find $\sum_{r=1}^{n} \dfrac{r+2}{2^{r+1}r(r+1)}$.

[**Hint**: Use partial fractions.]

18. Let $T = 1 + 2x + 3x^2 + \ldots + nx^{n-1} \ (x \neq 1)$. Find T

(i) by considering $T - xT$;

(ii) by summing $1 + x + x^2 + \ldots + x^n$ and then differentiating.

19. Find the sum to n terms of

$$\frac{1}{x+1} + \frac{2x}{(x+1)(x+2)} + \frac{3x^2}{(x+1)(x+2)(x+3)} + \ldots$$

[**Hint:** $nx^{n-1} = x^{n-1}(x+n) - x^n$]

20. An elegant proof for S_2

(i) Using the array on the right, or otherwise, prove that

$$r^2 = 1 + 2 + 3 + \ldots + (r-1) + r + (r-1) + \ldots + 3 + 2 + 1.$$

(ii) Show that $\displaystyle\sum_{r=1}^{5} r^2$ is the sum of the numbers in any

one of the three arrays below.

(a)   (b)   (c)

(iii) Now slide (a) and (c) on top of (b) so that they overlap as shown by the shading, and add overlapping numbers. Deduce that

$$3\sum_{r=1}^{5} r^2 = 11\sum_{r=1}^{5} r.$$

(iv) Generalise this argument to show that $3S_2 = (2n+1)S_1$ and deduce that

$$S_2 = \tfrac{1}{6}n(n+1)(2n+1)$$

21. (i) Copy and complete this table.

n	S_1	S_2	S_4	$5S_4/S_2$	$6S_1$
1					
2					
3					
4					
5					

Hence find and prove a formula for S_4 in terms of n.

(ii) Prove that S_4 is divisible by S_2 if and only if $n = 5m + 1$ or $n = 5m + 3$, where $m \geqslant 0$.

(iii) Investigate the values of n for which S_4 is divisible by S_1.

KEY POINTS

The flow of a proof is shown by the symbols $\Rightarrow$, $\Leftarrow$, $\Leftrightarrow$ or by the correct use of 'if', 'only if', 'necessary', 'sufficient' as follows

$P \Rightarrow Q$	P is a sufficient condition for Q	P only if Q
$P \Leftarrow Q$	P is a necessary condition for Q	P if Q
$P \Leftrightarrow Q$	P is a necessary and sufficient condition for Q	P if and only if Q

- The *converse* of $P \Rightarrow Q$ is $P \Leftarrow Q$ or $Q \Rightarrow P$.

- To prove *P by contradiction*, show that assuming P to be false leads to a contradiction.

- A general statement can be disproved by a single *counter-example*, but cannot be proved by any number of verifications unless these exhaust all the possibilities.

- To prove *by induction* that a statement (C) involving an integer n is true for all $n \geqslant n_0$, prove that

  (i) (C) is true for $n = n_0$;

  (ii) if (C) is true for $n = k$ then (C) is true for $n = k + 1$.

  and then bring these parts together to complete the proof.

- $$\sum_{r=1}^{n} r = \tfrac{1}{2}n(n+1) \qquad \sum_{r=1}^{n} r^2 = \tfrac{1}{6}n(n+1)(2n+1) \qquad \sum_{r=1}^{n} r^3 = \tfrac{1}{4}n^2(n+1)^2$$

- If $u_r = v_r - v_{r-1}$ for $r = 1, 2, ..., n$ then $\displaystyle\sum_{r=1}^{n} u_r = v_n - v_0$ (a telescoping sum). Partial fractions can be useful when finding v_r.

Graphs and inequalities

Every picture is worth a thousand words.

Traditional Chinese proverb

Our culture is a visual one: we increasingly expect pictures or diagrams to illustrate ideas. Good diagrams not only help writers to communicate efficiently, but they also help students and researchers to discover and understand relationships.

You have been introduced to sketching graphs in Pure Mathematics 1 and 2. You will know that a sketch graph should show the essential features of the graph, such as where it cuts the axes, the nature and position of turning points, any symmetry, and the behaviour of the graph as x or y tends to infinity. We shall often be satisfied with approximate location rather than exact positions. In this chapter we use calculus as little as possible.

Whether you have a graphics calculator or not, aim to be able to produce your own sketch graphs without being dependent on the calculator. To be able to sketch the graph of a function accurately without using a machine demonstrates a good appreciation of the behaviour of that function. Learning to draw such sketches will help you realise how various functions behave, and why they behave like that. If you have ready access to a graphics calculator (or graph-drawing software) use it to check your sketches.

The most basic technique for drawing the graph of a function $f(x)$ is 'dot-to-dot': choose values of x and calculate each corresponding value of $f(x)$, usually called y, and plot these (x, y) values as points, joining them up in order of increasing x. Accuracy is improved by plotting more points, concentrating particularly on the regions where you are least certain, perhaps where the curve bends most.

Graphics calculators and graph-drawing computer programs draw graphs rapidly, many using 'dot-to-dot' methods. Sometimes the operator has the opportunity to adjust the *resolution* (or step between successive dots): smaller steps produce more accurate graphs. Even when using small steps the display should be interpreted carefully as some programs wrongly connect together separate branches of a curve.

Activity

If you have access to a graphics calculator or graph-drawing program on a computer use it to draw the graph of $y = \frac{1}{x}$ from $x = -4$ to $x = 4$ and compare the display with the diagrams. Try changing the x range, or the resolution.

The incorrect diagram was the output from a computer graph-drawing package.

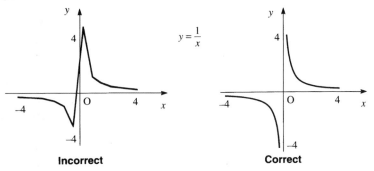

Incorrect　　　　　　　　**Correct**

For Discussion

(i) Why is it wrong to join the two branches of $y = \frac{1}{x}$?

(ii) Is it better to join dots with straight lines or with curves?

(iii) Why don't graphics calculators display smooth curves?

Even if your graphics calculator does produce less than perfect graphs, don't throw it away! Ability to control and correctly interpret its display turns it into a valuable tool. Adjusting the *range* of the display – effectively adjusting the width and height of the window through which the graph is viewed – changes the horizontal and vertical scales. Most calculators allow you to zoom in or out. Some allow you to scroll horizontally or vertically. Unfortunately the controls are not yet standardised across the various makes of calculator, so it is inappropriate to describe them in detail here. But do experiment with them, so that you learn to use them to advantage, paying particular attention to the range controls.

Graphs of rational functions

A rational number is defined as a number which can be expressed as $\frac{n}{d}$, where the numerator n and denominator d are integers, and $d \neq 0$. In a similar way a *rational function* is defined as a function which can be expressed in the form $\frac{N(x)}{D(x)}$, where the numerator, $N(x)$, and denominator,

$D(x)$, are polynomials, and $D(x)$ is not the zero polynomial. In this section we concentrate on how to sketch graphs of rational functions.

Consider the graph of $y = \frac{1}{x}$. If you translate it three units to the right and two units up you obtain the graph of $y = \frac{1}{x-3} + 2$ which can be re-arranged as $y = \frac{2x-5}{x-3}$ (see figure 2.1.)

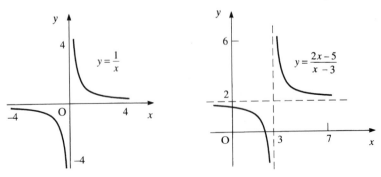

Figure 2.1

Now consider yourself moving along the curve $y = \frac{2x-5}{x-3}$. As your x co-ordinate gets close to 3, your y co-ordinate tends to $\pm\infty$, and you get closer and closer to the vertical line $x = 3$, shown pecked. If you move along the curve again, letting your x co-ordinate increase without limit (or decrease without limit) you get closer and closer to the horizontal line $y = 2$, also shown pecked. These pecked lines are examples of asymptotes. An asymptote is a straight line which a curve approaches tangentially as x and/or y tend to infinity. The line $x = 3$ is a vertical asymptote; the line $y = 2$ is a horizontal asymptote. It is usual for asymptotes to be shown by pecked lines.

In general, the line $x = a$ is a vertical asymptote for the curve $y = \frac{N(x)}{D(x)}$ if $D(a) = 0$ and $N(a) \neq 0$. The signs of the numerator $N(x)$ and the denominator $D(x)$ when x is close to a enable us to determine whether y tends to positive or negative infinity as x tends to a from left or from right. We illustrate this in sub-section (b) opposite.

Sketching the graph of $y = \frac{x+2}{(x-2)(x+1)}$

We show below the steps we have used in building up the sketch graph.

(a) Find where the graph cuts the axes

The *y intercept* is where the graph cuts the y axis. We find it by evaluating y when $x = 0$: in the case of our equation $y = \dfrac{x+2}{(x-2)(x+1)}$ the y intercept is $(0, -1)$.

The x *intercept* is where the graph cuts the x axis. To find it, we put $y = 0$, and solve the resulting equation, getting, in this case, just one root, $x = -2$. We now know that this graph passes through $(0, -1)$ and $(-2, 0)$ and does not cut the axes anywhere else.

(b) Examine the behaviour of the graph near the vertical asymptotes

The denominator of $\dfrac{x+2}{(x-2)(x+1)}$ is zero when $x = -1$ or 2, but these values do not make the numerator zero, so the vertical asymptotes are the lines $x = -1$ and $x = 2$. To examine the behaviour near $x = -1$, we look at the three terms $(x + 2)$, $(x - 2)$ and $(x + 1)$, paying particular attention to their signs (figure 2.2).

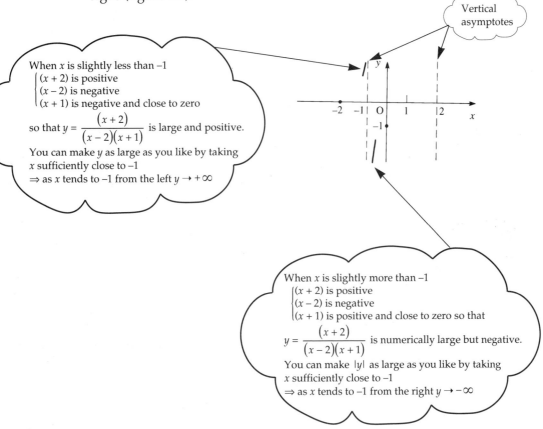

Vertical asymptotes

When x is slightly less than -1
$(x + 2)$ is positive
$(x - 2)$ is negative
$(x + 1)$ is negative and close to zero

so that $y = \dfrac{(x+2)}{(x-2)(x+1)}$ is large and positive.
You can make y as large as you like by taking x sufficiently close to -1
$\Rightarrow$ as x tends to -1 from the left $y \to +\infty$

When x is slightly more than -1
$(x + 2)$ is positive
$(x - 2)$ is negative
$(x + 1)$ is positive and close to zero so that

$y = \dfrac{(x+2)}{(x-2)(x+1)}$ is numerically large but negative.
You can make $|y|$ as large as you like by taking x sufficiently close to -1
$\Rightarrow$ as x tends to -1 from the right $y \to -\infty$

Figure 2.2

You can use a similar method to examine the behaviour of the graph as it approaches its other vertical asymptote, $x = 2$. You will find that $y \to -\infty$ as $x \to 2$ from the left and $y \to +\infty$ as $x \to 2$ from the right. Figure 2.3 shows the details obtained so far.

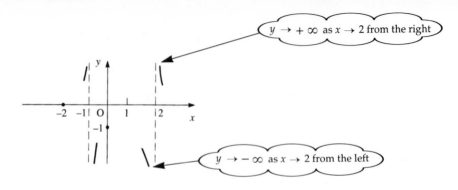

Figure 2.3

(c) Examine the behaviour as x tends to infinity

Now

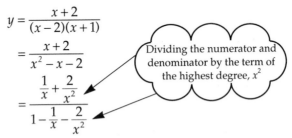

$$y = \frac{x+2}{(x-2)(x+1)}$$

$$= \frac{x+2}{x^2-x-2}$$

$$= \frac{\frac{1}{x}+\frac{2}{x^2}}{1-\frac{1}{x}-\frac{2}{x^2}}$$

Dividing the numerator and denominator by the term of the highest degree, x^2

which tends to 0 as $x \to \infty$ because $\frac{1}{x}$ and $\frac{2}{x^2} \to 0$ as $x \to \infty$.

Further, as $(x + 2)$, $(x - 2)$ and $(x + 1)$ are all positive for large, positive x, $y \to 0$ from above as $x \to +\infty$. Similarly $y \to 0$ from below as $x \to -\infty$. The line $y = 0$ is a horizontal asymptote (figure 2.4).

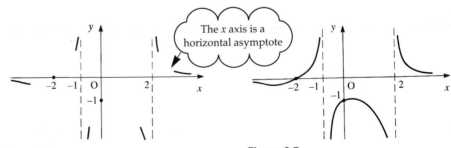

The x axis is a horizontal asymptote

Figure 2.4   **Figure 2.5**

(d) Complete the sketch

The sketch is completed in figure 2.5. Notice that this leads us to conclude that there is a local maximum between $x = -1$ and $x = 2$, and a local minimum to the left of $x = 2$. We do not know the y co-ordinate of either the minimum or the maximum. Nor have we shown that there are no other turning points, but see below for more on that subject. If we needed to locate the stationary points precisely we could differentiate; then solving $\frac{dy}{dx} = 0$ would tell us that there are only two turning points, at $x = 0$ and at $x = -4$.

How many turning points?

We based our sketch of $y = \dfrac{x+2}{(x-2)(x+1)}$ on the information shown here in figure 2.6(a).

(a)

Can we be sure that there are only two turning points, as we chose to sketch it – see figure 2.6(b)?

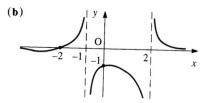

(b)

How do we know that figure 2.6(c), with additional turning points, is wrong?

In answer to these questions we look at two ways we could solve the equation $Y = \dfrac{x+2}{(x-2)(x+1)}$ where Y is a given value.

(c)

(i) We could draw graphs and observe where the horizontal line $y = Y$ meets the curve $y = \dfrac{x+2}{(x-2)(x+1)}$.

Figure 2.6

(ii) Alternatively, we could multiply both sides by $(x-2)(x+1)$, getting

$$(x-2)(x+1)Y = x + 2$$

which is a quadratic equation in x (unless $Y = 0$).

It may have

- no roots, corresponding to line A (figure 2.7) not meeting the curve;

- or one root (i.e. repeated roots) – see line B;

- or two distinct roots – see lines C and D.

Figure 2.7

The quadratic equation cannot have more than two roots: a horizontal line cannot meet the curve in more than two places. But lines E and F each meet the curve four times, a clear contradiction.

We already know we have a (local) maximum between $x = -1$ and $x = 2$ and a (local) minimum to the left of $x = -2$. Each additional turning point increases (by 2) the number of times the curve meets a horizontal line which already intersects the curve. We cannot have additional turning points.

P4

Incidentally, this argument also tells us that the maximum must be lower than the minimum.

Activity

Sketch the graph of (a) $y = \dfrac{3x-6}{(x+2)(x-3)}$; (b) $y = \dfrac{x-2}{(x-1)^2}$.

In (b) be careful about what happens near the vertical asymptote.

When we examined the behaviour of $y = \dfrac{x+2}{(x-2)(x+1)}$ as x tends to infinity, we divided numerator and denominator by the highest power of x. A similar argument shows that if the numerator of a rational function is of lower degree than the denominator then $y = 0$ is a horizontal asymptote. If the numerator has the same degree as the denominator, we can use the same method, as in the following example, but notice how we get more information if we divide the numerator by the denominator first.

EXAMPLE   Sketch the graph of $y = \dfrac{(x-2)(6-x)}{(x+1)(x-4)}$.

Solution

$$y = \frac{(x-2)(6-x)}{(x+1)(x-4)}$$

$$= \frac{-x^2 + 8x - 12}{x^2 - 3x - 4}$$

$$= \frac{-1 + \dfrac{8}{x} - \dfrac{12}{x^2}}{1 - \dfrac{3}{x} - \dfrac{4}{x^2}}$$

> Dividing top and bottom by x^2

which tends to -1 as $x \to \pm\infty$, indicating that the line $y = -1$ is a horizontal asymptote.

Dividing the numerator ($-x^2 + 8x - 12$) by the denominator ($x^2 - 3x - 4$), we get

$$y = -1 + \frac{5x - 16}{(x+1)(x-4)}$$

When x is large and positive ($5x - 16$), ($x + 1$) and ($x - 4$) are positive so that y is slightly more than -1; we say: $y \to -1$ from above as $x \to +\infty$.

When x is numerically large but negative these three terms are negative so that y is slightly less than -1; we say: $y \to -1$ from below as $x \to -\infty$.

(Alternatively, evaluate y for numerically large x, such as $x = 100$ and $x = -100$.

The graph cuts the y axis at $(0, 3)$, and the x axis at $(2, 0)$ and at $(6, 0)$. The vertical asymptotes are $x = -1$ and $x = 4$.

As $x \to -1$ from the left, $y \to -\infty$; as $x \to -1$ from the right, $y \to +\infty$.

As $x \to 4$ from the left, $y \to -\infty$; as $x \to 4$ from the right, $y \to +\infty$.

All this information is included on the sketch graph.

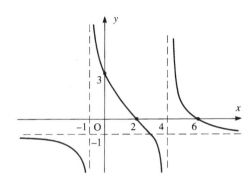

The equation $y = \dfrac{(x-2)(6-x)}{(x+1)(x-4)}$ is equivalent to a quadratic in x, so each horizontal line (except the asymptote $y = -1$) will cross the graph at most twice. There cannot be any stationary points.

In the last example the information about the behaviour near the vertical asymptotes was in fact superfluous: we could have drawn our sketch using only the intercepts and the behaviour as $x \to \infty$. It did, however, provide confirmation that the sketch was correct.

Recognising symmetry can help us to draw a sketch. If $f(x) = f(-x)$ the graph of $y = f(x)$ is symmetrical about the y axis, and f is an *even* function – see Pure Mathematics 2, page 82; functions containing only even powers of x are even functions. If $f(x) = -f(-x)$ the graph of $y = f(x)$ has rotational symmetry of order 2 about the origin; in this case f is an *odd* function.

EXAMPLE

Sketch the graph of $y = f(x)$, where $f(x) = \dfrac{x^2 + 1}{x^2 + 2}$.

Solution

When $x = 0$ $y = \frac{1}{2}$ so the graph passes through $(0, \frac{1}{2})$.

No (real) value of x makes $x^2 + 1 = 0$, so the graph does not cut the x axis.

No (real) value of x makes $x^2 + 2 = 0$, so there are no vertical asymptotes.

Now $y = \dfrac{x^2 + 1}{x^2 + 2} = 1 - \dfrac{1}{x^2 + 2}$ so $y \to 1$ from below as $x \to \pm\infty$.

As $f(x)$ contains only even powers of x, f is an even function and the graph is symmetrical about the y axis (see diagram).

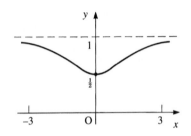

Symmetry considerations tell us that the graph is stationary at $(0, \frac{1}{2})$.

As $y = \dfrac{x^2 + 1}{x^2 + 2}$ is effectively a quadratic equation in x, no horizontal line will cross the graph more than twice, so we cannot have any other turning points. (Differentiation will also confirm that $(0, \frac{1}{2})$ is the only stationary point.)

As shown in the next example, a somewhat similar approach allows us to deal with rational functions with numerator of higher degree than denominator.

EXAMPLE Sketch the graph of $y = \dfrac{x^2 - 2}{x - 1}$.

Solution

Dividing numerator by denominator we get

$$y = \frac{x^2 - 2}{x - 1}$$

$$= x + 1 - \frac{1}{x - 1}$$

Since $\dfrac{1}{x - 1} \to 0$ as $x \to \pm\infty$, when x is numerically large y is

approximately $x + 1$; thus the graph of $y = \dfrac{x^2 - 2}{x - 1}$ approaches the line $y = x + 1$ asymptotically as $x \to \pm\infty$. The line $y = x + 1$ is an oblique asymptote. When x is large and positive the graph of $y = \dfrac{x^2 - 2}{x - 1}$ is just below $y = x + 1$;

when x is numerically large but negative the graph of $y = \dfrac{x^2 - 2}{x - 1}$ is slightly above $y = x + 1$.

The graph cuts the x axis when $x = \pm\sqrt{2}$ (i.e. when $x \approx \pm 1.41$). The vertical asymptote is $x = 1$, with $y \to +\infty$ as $x \to 1$ from the left and $y \to -\infty$ as $x \to 1$ from the right.

The graph is as sketched in the diagram on page 37.

There are no stationary points as $y = \dfrac{x^2 - 2}{x - 1}$ is effectively a quadratic equation in x, so that horizontal lines can cut the curve at most twice.

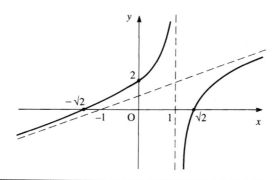

Exercise 2A

Sketch the graphs in questions 1 – 18.

1. $y = \dfrac{2}{x - 3}$

2. $y = \dfrac{2}{(x - 3)^2}$

3. $y = \dfrac{x - 5}{(x + 2)(x - 3)}$

4. $y = \dfrac{3 - x}{(2 - x)(4 - x)}$

5. $y = \dfrac{x}{x^2 - 4}$

6. $y = \dfrac{x - 3}{(x - 4)^2}$

7. $y = \dfrac{x^2(x - 2)}{x^2 - 1}$

8. $y = \dfrac{(2x - 3)(5x + 2)}{(x + 1)(x - 4)}$

9. $y = \dfrac{x(x - 1)}{x + 1}$

10. $y = \dfrac{x^2 + 3}{x - 2}$

11. $y = \dfrac{(x - 4)(x - 1)}{x - 2}$

12. $y = \dfrac{1}{x^2 + 1}$

13. $y = \dfrac{x}{x^2 + 3}$

14. $y = \dfrac{4 - x^2}{4 + x^2}$

15. $y = \dfrac{x^3 - 8}{x^2 + 1}$

16. $y = \dfrac{x^3 + 1}{x - 1}$

17. $y = \dfrac{x^2 - 6x + 9}{x^2 + 1}$

18. $y = \dfrac{x^2 - 5x - 6}{(x + 1)(x - 4)}$

[Be careful!]

19. The concentration y of a drug in the blood x hours after it has been administered is modelled by $y = \dfrac{x}{20x^2 + 50x + 80}$. Sketch the graph for $x \geqslant 0$. When does the maximum concentration occur?

20. Describe the symmetry of the graph of $y = \dfrac{x^4 - x^2 + 2}{x^4 + 1}$ and locate its asymptotes. Sketch the graph.

Exercise 2A continued

21. The police use a radar 'gun' to measure the speed of approaching vehicles. The gun is both transmitter and receiver, transmitting at frequency f (usually about 10 GHz) and receiving part of the radar beam reflected from the moving vehicle. The gun measures b, the difference in the frequencies of the transmitted and reflected beams. The speed u of the vehicle is modelled by $u = \dfrac{cb}{b+f}$, where c is the speed of light, about 3×10^8 m s^{-1}. Sketch the graph of u against b. What difference does it make to the gradient of the relevant part of the graph if the police decrease the value of f?

22. When a camera with lens of focal length F mm and aperture f is focused on an object which is d mm from the camera other objects may also appear acceptably sharp. The region of acceptable sharpness is known as the *depth of field*. The near limit of the depth of field is d_{near} mm and the far limit (if there is one) is d_{far} mm, where

$$d_{near} = \frac{d}{1+0.025df/F^2} \text{ and } d_{far} = \frac{d}{1-0.025df/F^2} \text{ (provided } F^2 > 0.025df).$$

The aperture f is usually one of the numbers $1.4, 2, 2.8, 4, 5.6, 8, 11, 16, 22, \ldots$ where a large number represents a small aperture, and vice versa. Sketch d_{near} and d_{far} against positive f, for fixed d, taking $F = 50$. Explain why landscape photographers frequently choose a small aperture, while portrait photographers often choose a comparatively large aperture.

23. Sketch the graph of $y = \dfrac{x}{x^2-9}$.

    (i) Show how the equation can be rearranged as a quadratic equation in x, provided $y \neq 0$.

    (ii) If y is given (and is not 0), how many values of x can be found?

    (iii) The graph is continuous for x between -3 and 3. What happens to y as x varies from -3 to 3? Explain why there are no turning points between $x = -3$ and $x = 3$.

    (iv) Explain why the graph has no turning points anywhere.

24. Without using calculus explain why the graph of $y = \dfrac{x-2}{x+3}$ has no turning points.

25. Show that $y = \dfrac{(x-b)}{(x-a)(x-c)}$ has no turning points if $a < b < c$.
    What happens if $a = c$ and $b < a$?

Graphs of $y^2 = f(x)$

Activity

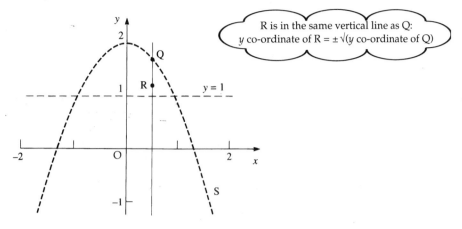

R is in the same vertical line as Q:
y co-ordinate of R = $\pm \sqrt{(y}$ co-ordinate of Q)

In the diagram, the pecked curve (labelled S) is the graph of $y = 2 - x^2$.

(i)   Copy the diagram, mark (fairly accurately) several possible positions for R, and sketch the locus of R as Q moves along curve S.

(ii) Describe the position of R relative to Q when the y co-ordinate of R is positive and

    (a) Q is above the line $y = 1$;

    (b) Q is on the line $y = 1$;

    (c) Q is between the x axis and the line $y = 1$.

(iii) What happens when Q is below the x axis?

(iv) Explain why the locus of R is a complete circle.

The locus of R constructed in the activity above is the circle with equation $y^2 = 2 - x^2$. It is symmetrical about the x axis, a property of all curves representing equations of the form $y^2 = f(x)$. This is because if (x_1, y_1) satisfies $y^2 = f(x)$, then $(x_1, -y_1)$ also satisfies the equation. Notice, too, that the graph only exists for values of x which make $f(x) \geqslant 0$.

The curve representing $y^2 = f(x)$ can cross the x axis in a number of ways. We illustrate two of these in the following example.

EXAMPLE   Sketch curve C, the graph of $y^2 = x^2(x + 2)$.

Solution

First we sketch the graph of $y = x^2 (x + 2)$ obtaining curve S, shown pecked in the diagram on page 40. Each point (such as Q) on S above the x axis gives rise to two points (R and R′) on C, symmetrically arranged about the x axis: R is always nearer to $y = 1$ than Q, and R' is the image of R by reflection in the x axis.

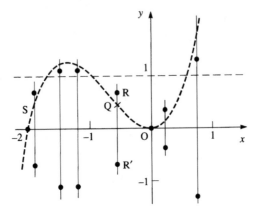

As S intersects the x axis at $(-2, 0)$ and at $(0, 0)$, C also intersects the x axis at these points. We now look more carefully at the gradient of C at these two points:

$$y^2 = x^2(x + 2) \implies y = \pm x\sqrt{x+2}$$

$$\implies \frac{dy}{dx} = \pm\left[\sqrt{x+2} + x.\tfrac{1}{2}(x+2)^{-\frac{1}{2}}\right]$$

$$\implies \frac{dy}{dx} = \pm\left(\sqrt{x+2} + \frac{x}{2\sqrt{x+2}}\right)$$

Using the product and chain rules

As $x \to -2$ from the right, $\dfrac{dy}{dx} \to \pm\infty$ so that at $(-2, 0)$ the tangent to C is parallel to the y axis.

However at $(0, 0)$, $\dfrac{dy}{dx} \to \pm\sqrt{2}$, so we complete the sketch as shown below.

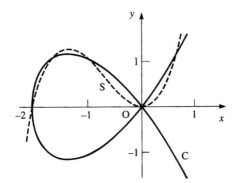

Alternatively, we could use the fact that near the origin

$$y^2 = x^2(x + 2) \implies y^2 \approx 2x^2 \implies y \approx \pm\sqrt{2}x.$$

Differentiating the general equation $y^2 = f(x)$ with respect to x gives

$$2y \frac{dy}{dx} = f'(x)$$

If the curve C with equation $y^2 = f(x)$ meets the x axis at the point $P(x_1, 0)$ two possibilities arise:

either $f'(x_1) \neq 0$ in which case the tangent to C at P is parallel to the y axis, as at $(-2, 0)$ in the example above;

or $f'(x_1) = 0$ in which case the direction of the tangent at P depends on the particular function f. You will need to treat each such case separately.

Thus the curve C representing $y^2 = f(x)$ crosses the x axis at $(x_1, 0)$ where $f(x_1) = 0$; the tangent to C at the point $(x_1, 0)$ is vertical unless $f'(x_1) = 0$.

Exercise 2B

Sketch the graphs in Questions 1 – 6.

1. $y^2 = (x + 2)(x - 1)(x - 4)$

2. $y^2 = \frac{1}{12} x^3 (4 - x)$

3. $y^2 = x^4(x + 2)$

4. $y^2 = \dfrac{x}{1 + x^2}$

5. $y^2 = \dfrac{x^2}{x^2 - 1}$

6. $y^2 = \dfrac{x^2 - 1}{x^2 - 4}$

7. Sketch the graph of the equation $y^2 = x^3$. This is known as the *semi-cubical parabola*.

8. On one set of axes sketch the graphs of $y^2 = 3x - x^3 + c$ for $c = 4, 2, 0, -2, -4$.

9. A curve has equation $y = x + 2 + \dfrac{4}{x - 3}$.

   (i) Calculate the co-ordinates of the points where the curve crosses the y axis and the x axis.

   (ii) Find $\dfrac{dy}{dx}$, and hence calculate the co-ordinates of the two stationary points on the curve.

   (iii) Explain how the curve is related to the line $y = x + 2$.

   (iv) Sketch the curve, together with its asymptotes.

   (v) On a separate diagram, sketch the curve with equation

   $$y^2 = x + 2 + \frac{4}{x - 3}$$

   Indicate clearly the co-ordinates of the points where this curve crosses the axes, and the stationary points.

   [MEI 1994]

Graphs of $y = |f(x)|$

When sketching the graph of $y = |2 - x^2|$ it is again helpful to start by sketching the curve S with equation $y = 2 - x^2$. As $|n| = -n$ if $n < 0$, any part of S which is below the x axis is reflected in the x axis to form part of the graph of $y = |2 - x^2|$ (see figure 2.8); any part of S which is above the x axis forms part of the graph of $y = |2 - x^2|$ without alteration.

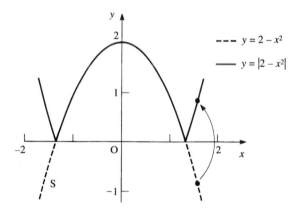

Figure 2.8

EXAMPLE

Sketch the graph of $y = \left| \dfrac{x+2}{(x-2)(x+1)} \right|$.

Solution

We developed the sketch of $y = \dfrac{x+2}{(x-2)(x+1)}$ in figure 2.5 on page 32.

We show it again here: sections which are above the x axis have been drawn with a continuous curve, while sections which are below the x axis have been drawn pecked.

The pecked sections (below the x axis) are reflected in the x axis, the image being drawn with a continuous curve.

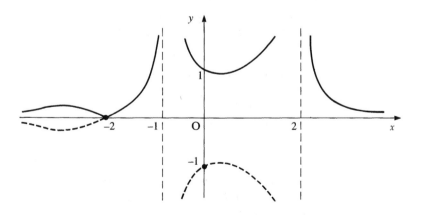

The graph of $y = \left| \dfrac{x+2}{(x-2)(x+1)} \right|$ is shown by the continuous curve above.

It should be noted that at $(-2, 0)$ the curve is cusped and not smooth.

Exercise 2C

Sketch the graphs in Questions 1 – 6.

1. $y = |x(x-1)(x-2)|$ **2.** $y = \left| \dfrac{x}{x+1} \right|$

3. $y = \left| \dfrac{1-x^2}{x^2-4} \right|$ **4.** $y = \left| \dfrac{x-1}{x^2+1} \right|$

5. $y = |\sin x|$ **6.** $y = \left| \dfrac{x(x-1)}{x-2} \right|$

7. On the same axes sketch the graphs of $y = \left| \dfrac{1}{2+x} \right|$ and $y = \left| \dfrac{x}{x-5} \right|$.

How many roots does the equation $\left| \dfrac{1}{2+x} \right| = \left| \dfrac{x}{x-5} \right|$ have?

8. Sketch the curve whose equation is $y = f(x) = \dfrac{(x-4)(x-1)}{x(x-5)}$ stating the equations of its asymptotes. Find the co-ordinates of any stationary points and explain how their nature might be determined. Sketch on separate diagrams the curves with equations (i) $y^2 = f(x)$, and (ii) $y = |f(x)|$.

[MEI 1992]

Inequalities

An *inequality* is a statement involving one of the order relationships $<, >, \leqslant, \geqslant$. There are two types of inequality:

- those whose truth depends on the value of the variable involved, and
- those which are always true.

For example: the statement $x^2 > 4$ is true if and only if $x < -2$ or $x > 2$,

whereas: the statement $(x-3)^2 + y^2 \geqslant 0$ is true for all real values of x and y.

With the first type of inequality our task is usually to find the set of values for which the inequality is true; this is called *solving the inequality*. With the second type we usually want to prove that the statement is always true. This distinction is similar to that between solving an equation, such as $x^2 = 4$, and proving an identity, such as $(p+q)^2 \equiv p^2 + 2pq + q^2$. We distinguish between equations and identities by using the different symbols = and ≡; but with inequalities we have to use the same symbols in both situations.

The basic statement $x > y$ can be interpreted in two simple ways:

$x > y \iff$ the point representing x is to the right of the point representing y on the standard number line;

$x > y \iff x - y$ is positive.

Either interpretation can be used to justify the familiar basic rules for manipulating inequalities.

	Rule	Example (based on 'is greater than')
1	You may add the same number to each side of an inequality	$x > y \iff x + a > y + a$
2	You may multiply (or divide) both sides of an inequality by the same positive number	If p is positive: $x > y \iff px > py$
3	If both sides of an inequality are multiplied (or divided) by the same negative number the inequality is reversed	If n is negative: $x > y \iff nx < ny$
4	You may add (but not subtract) corresponding sides of inequalities of the same type	$a > b$ and $x > y \implies a + x > b + y$
5	Inequalities of the same type are *transitive*	$x > y$ and $y > z \implies x > z$

Similar definitions apply to each of the inequalities $>, <, \geq, \leq$, and the same basic rules can be proved from the definitions.

EXAMPLE

Starting from the definition that $x > y$ means that $x - y$ is positive, prove Rule 3, that if n is negative, $x > y \iff nx < ny$.

Solution

$$x > y \iff x - y \text{ is positive}$$
$$\iff n(x - y) \text{ is negative as } n \text{ is negative}$$
$$\iff nx - ny \text{ is negative}$$
$$\iff nx < ny$$

Activity

Use the number line and/or the properties of positive and negative numbers to justify Rules 1, 2, 4 and 5. Include counter-examples to show that inequalities may not be subtracted.

An obvious method of solving an inequality such as $f(x) > 0$ is to use the graph of $y = f(x)$: the solution is then the set of values of x for which the graph is above the x axis. Similarly, when solving $g(x) \leq h(x)$ you could draw the graphs of $y = g(x)$ and $y = h(x)$ and find the values of x where the first graph intersects or is lower than the second graph. But unless the graphs are already drawn, or are required for another purpose, it is usually quicker to use a mixture of algebra and simpler graphs as illustrated in the following examples.

EXAMPLE Solve the inequality $\dfrac{x^2 - 2}{x - 1} \leq 0$.

Solution 1

Sketch the curve $y = \dfrac{x^2 - 2}{x - 1}$, as shown here. (We sketched this graph on page 36.) From the graph we can see that $y \leq 0$ when $x \leq -\sqrt{2}$ or $1 < x \leq \sqrt{2}$.

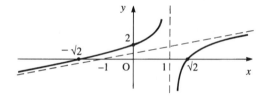

Solution 2

If we want to multiply the inequality by $x - 1$, we have problems as we do not know whether $x - 1$ is positive or negative: we need to consider both possibilities. A better method is to multiply by $(x - 1)^2$, which we know is positive, obtaining $(x^2 - 2)(x - 1) \leq 0$, $x - 1 \neq 0$.

Now the sketch of $y = (x^2 - 2)(x - 1)$ allows us to read off the solutions.

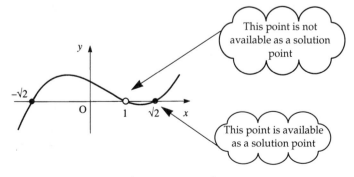

This point is not available as a solution point

This point is available as a solution point

Again we obtain $x \leq -\sqrt{2}$ or $1 < x \leq \sqrt{2}$. (Note exclusion of $x = 1$.)

Solution 3

As the value of x changes, a function $f(x)$ can only change its sign as x passes through a value where $f(x) = 0$ or where $f(x)$ is undefined. These values of x are know as *critical points*. We can solve an inequality by checking the truth of the inequality at and on either side of these critical points.

For $\dfrac{x^2 - 2}{x - 1} \leqslant 0$ the critical points are where we have equality (at $x = \pm\sqrt{2}$)

and where $\dfrac{x^2 - 2}{x - 1}$ is undefined (at $x = 1$). We now test whether the

inequality is true or not in the various regions. (**Y** indicates that inequality is true.)

	$x < -\sqrt{2}$	$x = -\sqrt{2}$	$-\sqrt{2} < x < 1$	$x = 1$	$1 < x < \sqrt{2}$	$x = \sqrt{2}$	$x > \sqrt{2}$
$\dfrac{x^2 - 2}{x - 1} \leqslant 0$	Y	Y	N	N	Y	Y	N

At $x = -2$, for example, $\dfrac{x^2 - 2}{x - 1}$ is negative

At $x = 0$ $\dfrac{x^2 - 2}{x - 1} = 2$

At $x = 2$ $\dfrac{x^2 - 2}{x - 1} = 2$

As before, the solution is $x \leqslant -\sqrt{2}$ or $1 < x \leqslant \sqrt{2}$.

When solving an inequality which involves two functions, such as $f(x) \leqslant g(x)$, it is usually good practice to re-arrange it in the equivalent form $f(x) - g(x) \leqslant 0$, as in the next example.

EXAMPLE

Solve the inequality $\dfrac{2x - 1}{x - 1} \leqslant \dfrac{9}{x + 1}$.

Solution

Provided $x \neq \pm 1$

Multiply by $(x - 1)^2(x + 1)^2$, which is positive

$$\dfrac{2x - 1}{x - 1} \leqslant \dfrac{9}{x + 1} \quad \Leftrightarrow \quad \dfrac{2x - 1}{x - 1} - \dfrac{9}{x + 1} \leqslant 0$$

$$\Leftrightarrow \quad (2x - 1)(x + 1)^2(x - 1) - 9(x - 1)^2(x + 1) \leqslant 0$$

$$\Leftrightarrow \quad (x + 1)(x - 1)[(2x - 1)(x + 1) - 9(x - 1)] \leqslant 0$$

$$\Leftrightarrow \quad (x + 1)(x - 1)(2x^2 - 8x + 8) \leqslant 0$$

$$\Leftrightarrow \quad 2(x + 1)(x - 1)(x - 2)^2 \leqslant 0$$

A sketch of $y = 2(x + 1)(x - 1)(x - 2)^2$ gives us the solution $-1 < x < 1$ or $x = 2$.

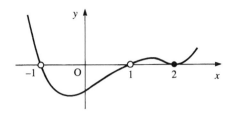

When solving inequalities involving modulus signs you can make use of the equivalents

$$|f(x)| \leqslant p \quad \Leftrightarrow \quad -p \leqslant f(x) \leqslant p \quad \Leftrightarrow \quad (f(x))^2 \leqslant p^2$$

but it is often simpler to use graphs.

EXAMPLE

Solve $3|x - 2| > x + 2$.

Solution

The graph of $y = 3|x - 2|$ consists of half-lines with gradients 3 and -3 starting from $(2, 0)$; these and the line $y = x + 2$ are as shown in the diagram.

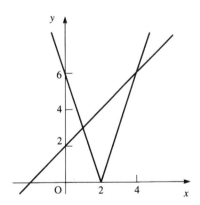

It is easy to verify that the points of intersection are $(1, 3)$ and $(4, 6)$.

The solution of the inequality is $x < 1$ or $x > 4$.

EXAMPLE

Solve the inequality $\left|\dfrac{x + 3}{x - 1}\right| \leqslant 2$.

Solution 1

$$\left|\frac{x + 3}{x - 1}\right| \leqslant 2 \quad \Leftrightarrow \quad -2 \leqslant \frac{x + 3}{x - 1} \leqslant 2$$

Then, provided $x \neq 1$

$$\frac{x+3}{x-1} \leqslant 2 \qquad \text{and} \qquad \frac{x+3}{x-1} \geqslant -2$$

$\Leftrightarrow \quad (x+3)(x-1) - 2(x-1)^2 \leqslant 0 \qquad \Leftrightarrow \quad (x+3)(x-1) + 2(x-1)^2 \geqslant 0$

$\Leftrightarrow \quad (x-1)[(x+3) - 2(x-1)] \leqslant 0 \qquad \Leftrightarrow \quad (x-1)[(x+3) + 2(x-1)] \geqslant 0$

$\Leftrightarrow \quad (x-1)(-x+5) \leqslant 0 \qquad\qquad \Leftrightarrow \quad (x-1)(3x+1) \geqslant 0$

$\Leftrightarrow \quad x < 1 \text{ or } x \geqslant 5 \qquad\qquad\quad \Leftrightarrow \quad x \leqslant -\frac{1}{3} \text{ or } x > 1$

We want the values of x which satisfy both inequalities: the solution is $x \leqslant -\frac{1}{3}$ or $x \geqslant 5$.

Solution 2

The same answer can be obtained more easily if we use the fact that

$$|f(x)| < k \qquad \Leftrightarrow \qquad (f(x))^2 < k^2$$

Thus, again provided $x \neq 1$,

$$\left|\frac{x+3}{x-1}\right| \leqslant 2 \quad \Leftrightarrow \quad \left(\frac{x+3}{x-1}\right)^2 \leqslant 4$$

$\Leftrightarrow \quad (x+3)^2 - 4(x-1)^2 \leqslant 0$

$\Leftrightarrow \quad -3x^2 + 14x + 5 \leqslant 0$

$\Leftrightarrow \quad -(3x+1)(x-5) \leqslant 0$

$\Leftrightarrow \quad x \leqslant -\frac{1}{3} \text{ or } x \geqslant 5$

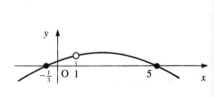

as shown in the diagram on the right.

Exercise 2D

Solve the inequalities in Questions 1 – 15.

1. $(x+3)(x-1)(2x-7) > 0$ **2.** $(x-1)(x-2)^2(x-3)^3 > 0$ **3.** $x^3 < x(3x+10)$

4. $\dfrac{(x-5)(x-2)}{x+1} \leqslant 0$ **5.** $\dfrac{5x-2}{(x+1)(x-2)} \geqslant 0$ **6.** $\dfrac{(x+2)(x-4)}{x(x-2)^2} \geqslant 0$

7. $\dfrac{x^2-2}{x-3} < 2$

8. $\dfrac{x^3-4}{x-2} \leqslant x+2$

9. $\dfrac{2x+3}{x-2} \leqslant 1$

10. $\dfrac{1}{x+6} \leqslant \dfrac{2}{2-3x}$

11. $|x+1| \geqslant |5-3x|$

12. $\left|\dfrac{2x+3}{x-2}\right| \leqslant 1$

13. $|2x-1| < 3x-1$

14. $\left|\dfrac{(x-1)(x-5)}{x-3}\right| \leqslant 3$

15. $\left|\dfrac{5-3x}{x+1}\right| \leqslant 1$

16. Rearrange $y = \dfrac{(x-2)(x+1)}{x^2}$ as a quadratic equation in x. (One of the coefficients will involve y.) Write down the condition for this equation to have real roots. Without using calculus, deduce the maximum value of y for real x.

17. Use the method of Question 16 to prove that, for real x,
$$1 \leqslant \dfrac{9x^2+8x+3}{x^2+1} \leqslant 11.$$

18. Find the set of possible values of $\dfrac{6x+6}{x^2+3}$ for real x.

19. Show that $\dfrac{x^2-2px+1}{px^2-2x+p}$ lies between -1 and 1 provided that p is not between -1 and 1.

Proving inequalities

Many inequalities which are always true can be derived from the basic fact that the square of a real number cannot be negative.

EXAMPLE Prove that if $x > 0$ and $y > 0$ then $\dfrac{x+y}{2} \geqslant \sqrt{(xy)}$.

Solution

Since x and y are positive we can let $p = \sqrt{x}$ and $q = \sqrt{y}$.

Then $(p-q)^2 \geqslant 0 \;\Rightarrow\; p^2+q^2 \geqslant 2pq$

$\Rightarrow\; x+y \geqslant 2\sqrt{x}\sqrt{y}$

$\Rightarrow\; \dfrac{x+y}{2} \geqslant \sqrt{(xy)}$

Pure Mathematics 4

NOTE

1. *Equality occurs if and only if p − q = 0, i.e. if and only if x = y.*

2. $\frac{x+y}{2}$ *is called the* arithmetic mean *of x and y, and $\sqrt{(xy)}$ is called the* geometric mean. *This example is the simplest case of an important inequality between the arithmetic and geometric means of any set of positive numbers (see Question 9 of Exercise 2E).*

EXAMPLE

Prove that if a, b, c are positive and not all equal then

$$(a + b + c)(bc + ca + ab) > 9abc$$

Solution

Expanding the left hand side gives

$$(a + b + c)(bc + ca + ab) = a(b^2 + c^2) + b(c^2 + a^2) + c(a^2 + b^2) + 3abc$$

and so

$$(a + b + c)(bc + ca + ab) - 9abc = a(b^2 + c^2) + b(c^2 + a^2) + c(a^2 + b^2) - 6abc$$
$$= a(b^2 - 2bc + c^2) + b(c^2 - 2ca + a^2) + c(a^2 - 2ab + b^2)$$
$$= a(b - c)^2 + b(c - a)^2 + c(a - b)^2$$

which is greater than zero, since the squares are not all zero.

Hence $(a + b + c)(bc + ca + ab) > 9abc$.

Exercise 2E

1. (i) Prove by two different methods that the sum of a positive number and its reciprocal is at least 2. (For example, use calculus or the result of the example on page 49.)

    (ii) Deduce that $\frac{q}{r} + \frac{r}{q} + \frac{r}{p} + \frac{p}{r} + \frac{p}{q} + \frac{q}{p} \geqslant 6$ for all positive p, q, r.

    When does equality occur?

2. (i) By considering $(a - b)^2 + (b - c)^2 + (c - a)^2$ prove that $a^2 + b^2 + c^2 \geqslant ab + bc + ca$ for all real a, b, c.

    (ii) Verify that $a^3 + b^3 + c^3 - 3abc = (a + b + c)(a^2 + b^2 + c^2 - ab - bc - ca)$.

    (iii) Let x, y, z be positive numbers. By putting $x = a^3$, etc., prove that $\frac{x+y+z}{3} \geqslant \sqrt[3]{xyz}$, with equality if and only if $x = y = z$.

3. Prove without using calculus that

    (a) of all rectangles with a given perimeter the square has the greatest area;

   (b) of all cuboids with a given surface area the cube has the greatest volume.

   [Use the results of the example on page 49 and Question 2 (iii)].

4. (i) Prove that $(x + y)^2 \geq 4xy$ for all values of x and y.

   (ii) Deduce that $\dfrac{1}{x} + \dfrac{1}{y} \geq \dfrac{4}{x+y}$ for all positive values of x and y.

     Give examples to show that if x and y are not both positive then the inequality is sometimes true and sometimes false.

5. The *harmonic mean*, H, and *root mean square*, R, of two positive numbers x, y are defined by $\dfrac{1}{H} = \dfrac{1}{2}\left(\dfrac{1}{x} + \dfrac{1}{y}\right)$ and $R = \sqrt{\dfrac{x^2 + y^2}{2}}$.

The arithmetic and geometric means are A and G respectively, as defined on page 50. Prove that $H \leq G$ and $R \geq A$.

6. The trapezium XX'Y'Y (see diagram) has parallel sides XX' $= x$ and YY' $= y$.

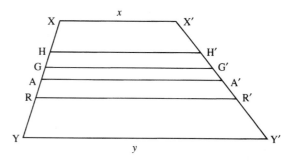

Prove the following results about lines drawn parallel to XX'.

(i) The arithmetic mean of x, y is AA', where AA' is midway between XX' and YY'.

(ii) The geometric mean of x, y is GG', where XX'G'G and GG'Y'Y are similar.

(iii) The harmonic mean of x, y is HH', where HH', XY', YX' are concurrent.

(iv) The root mean square of x, y is RR', where XX'R'R, RR'Y'Y have equal areas.

7. (i) Prove that $p^4 + q^4 \geq 2p^2q^2$ for all values of p and q.

   (ii) Prove that $p^4 + q^4 + r^4 + s^4 \geq 4pqrs$ for all positive values of p, q, r, s.

   (iii) Deduce that $\dfrac{w + x + y + z}{4} \geq \sqrt[4]{wxyz}$ for all positive values of w, x, y, z.

Exercise 2E continued

8. (i) Prove that $r(n - r + 1) > n \iff (r - 1)(r - n) < 0 \iff 1 < r < n$.

(ii) By writing $(n!)^2$ in the form $1.n.2.(n - 1).3.(n - 2) \ldots r.(n - r + 1) \ldots n.1$, deduce that $n! > \sqrt{(n^n)}$.

9. The arithmetic (A) and geometric (G) means of a set of n positive real numbers $x_1, x_2, \ldots, x_n$ are

$$A = \frac{x_1 + x_2 + \ldots + x_n}{n} \quad \text{and} \quad G = \sqrt[n]{x_1 x_2 \ldots x_n}$$

Let (C) be the statement that $A \geqslant G$; we have already seen in the example on page 49, Question 2 (iii) and Question 7 (iii) above that (C) is true when $n = 2, 3$ or 4.

(i) By letting $y_r = \dfrac{x_{2r-1} + x_{2r}}{2}$ and considering the arithmetic mean of the y_r, prove that if (C) is true when $n = k$ then (C) is true when $n = 2k$. Deduce that (C) is true when $n = 2^m$.

(ii) By considering the k numbers $x_1, x_2, \ldots, x_{k-1}, \dfrac{x_1 + x_2 + \ldots x_{k-1}}{k - 1}$, prove that if (C) is true when $n = k$ then (C) is true when $n = k - 1$.

(iii) Deduce that (C) is true for all integers $n \geqslant 2$. Under what conditions is there equality in (C)?

Investigations

1. Given that a, b, c, d and k are constants, investigate

(i) the form of the graph of $y = \dfrac{(x - a)(x - b)}{(x - c)(x - d)}$;

(ii) the number and location of solutions of the equation
$$\frac{(x - a)(x - b)}{(x - c)(x - d)} = k.$$

2. Investigate the shape of the graph of $y = \dfrac{ax^2 + bx + c}{Ax^2 + Bx + C}$ when

(i) $b^2 < 4ac$ and $B^2 = 4AC$

(ii) $b^2 \geqslant 4ac$ and $B^2 < 4AC$

(iii) $b^2 < 4ac$ and $B^2 > 4AC$

3. The Cauchy–Schwarz inequality

Let $x_1, x_2, \ldots, x_n$ and $y_1, y_2, \ldots, y_n$ be two sets of real numbers, and let
$$Q(t) = \sum_{r=1}^{n} (tx_r + y_r)^2, \text{ where } t \text{ is real.}$$

(i) Show that $Q(t) = At^2 + 2Bt + C$, where

$$A = \sum_{r=1}^{n} x_r^2 \qquad B = \sum_{r=1}^{n} x_r y_r \qquad C = \sum_{r=1}^{n} y_r^2$$

(ii) Explain why $Q(t) \geqslant 0$ for all t. Show that $Q(t) = 0$ if and only if there is a number λ such that $y_1 = \lambda x_1$, $y_2 = \lambda x_2$, ..., $y_n = \lambda x_n$ (i.e. the sequences $\{x_r\}$ and $\{y_r\}$ are proportional), and $t = -\lambda$. This shows that the quadratic equation $At^2 + 2Bt + C = 0$ has coincident roots if and only if the sequences $\{x_r\}$ and $\{y_r\}$ are proportional, and has no real roots otherwise.

(iii) Use the discriminant of this quadratic equation to deduce that

$$(x_1 y_1 + x_2 y_2 + ... + x_n y_n)^2 \leqslant (x_1^2 + x_2^2 + ... + x_n^2)(y_1^2 + y_2^2 + ... + y_n^2)$$

(This is the Cauchy–Schwarz inequality.)

(iv) Use the Cauchy-Schwarz inequality to prove that for any two vectors **x** and **y** in two or three dimensions the expression $\dfrac{\mathbf{x.y}}{|\mathbf{x}||\mathbf{y}|}$ must take a value between -1 and 1 (inclusive).This confirms that the equation $\cos\theta = \dfrac{\mathbf{x.y}}{|\mathbf{x}||\mathbf{y}|}$ can always be solved to find the angle θ between the two vectors. The same argument shows that the angle between vectors in higher dimensions can be defined by the same equation (see page 159).

(v) If you know about the product moment correlation coefficient (r) in statistics, use the Cauchy–Schwarz inequality to show that $-1 \leqslant r \leqslant 1$, and to interpret the extreme values.

KEY POINTS

- A *rational function* is a function which can be expressed in the form $\dfrac{N(x)}{D(x)}$, where the numerator, $N(x)$, and denominator, $D(x)$, are polynomials, and $D(x)$ is not the zero polynomial.

- To sketch the graph of $y = \dfrac{N(x)}{D(x)}$:

  (a) Find the intercepts, that is where the graph cuts the axes.

  (b) Examine the behaviour of the graph near the vertical asymptotes; these are the lines $x = a$ if $D(a) = 0$ and $N(a) \neq 0$.

  (c) Examine the behaviour as x tends to $\pm\infty$.

  (d) Show what you have found in (a), (b) and (c) on a sketch graph.

  (e) Complete the sketch.

- The graph of $y^2 = f(x)$ is symmetrical about the x axis. If the graph crosses the x axis at $(x_1, 0)$, the tangent to the curve at that point is parallel to the y axis unless $f'(x_1) = 0$. If $f'(x_1) = 0$ give special consideration to the value of the gradient.

- To sketch C, the graph of $y = |f(x)|$, first sketch S, the graph of $y = f(x)$: any parts of S which are above the x axis are also parts of C. Complete C by reflecting in the x axis any parts of S which are below the x axis.

- If you want to multiply (or divide) both sides of an inequality by some number you need to know its sign:

  * if p is positive: $x > y \iff px > py$

  * if n is negative: $x > y \iff nx < ny$

  When multiplying or dividing by a negative number, reverse the inequality.

- When solving inequalities involving rational functions, it can often be helpful to multiply by the square of the denominator (as this is automatically positive).

- For positive p, these three statements are equivalent:

$$|f(x)| \leq p \qquad -p \leq f(x) \leq p \qquad (f(x))^2 \leq p^2$$

3

Complex numbers

...that wonder of analysis, that portent of the ideal world, that amphibian between being and not-being, which we call the imaginary root of negative unity.

Leibniz, 1702

The growth of the number system

The number system with which you are familiar has taken many thousands of years to develop. In primitive societies all that are needed are the *counting numbers*, 1, 2, 3,... (or even just the first few of these), but with the growth of trade comes the concept of a *fraction*, first recorded in a systematic way in an Egyptian papyrus of about 1650 BC.

By 500 BC the Greeks had developed ways of calculating with whole numbers and their ratios (which accounts for calling fractions *rational* numbers). They also knew that between any two fractions, however close together they might be, it is always possible to find intermediate fractions (for example, the average of the two given fractions). So if we imagine the fractions represented by points on a number line, there is no segment of the line, however small, where there are no fractions: we express this by saying that the fractions are *dense*. Because of this the followers of Pythagoras believed that everything in geometry and in applications of mathematics could be explained in terms of rational numbers. It came as a great shock, therefore, when one of them proved that √2 is not a rational number (see page 8): legend has it that their reaction to this threat to their beliefs was to drown the discoverer. But then Greek thinkers gradually came to terms with the existence of such *irrational* numbers, and by 370 BC Eudoxus had devised a very careful theory of proportion which included both rational and irrational numbers.

It took about another thousand years for the next major development, when the Hindu mathematician Brahmagupta (about AD 630) described *negative* numbers, and gave the usual rules for dealing with negative signs. Surprisingly, the first use of a symbol for *zero* came even later, in AD 876. This was the final element needed to complete the set of *real* numbers, consisting of positive and negative rational and irrational numbers and zero; the real numbers can be represented by the points of the *real number line*.

For Discussion

How did your knowledge of the number system develop? Can you think of reasons for differences from the historical order?

Activity

Draw a single Venn diagram taking {real numbers} as the universal set, and showing the following subsets: {integers}, {rational numbers}, {irrational numbers}, {positive numbers}, {negative numbers}, {zero}. Show in your diagram the numbers 3, π, 355/113, −1, −1.4142, −$\sqrt{2}$. Draw also a real number line, and mark the same numbers on it.

The number system expanded in this way because people wanted to increase the range of problems they could tackle. This can be illustrated in terms of the sorts of equation that can be solved at each stage (though of course the standard algebraic way of writing these is relatively modern).

Activity

For each of these equations make up a simple problem that would lead to the equation, and say what sort of number is needed to solve the equation.

(i) $x + 7 = 10$

(ii) $7x = 10$

(iii) $x^2 = 10$

(iv) $x + 10 = 7$

(v) $x^2 + 7x = 0$

(vi) $x^2 + 10 = 0$

You will have hit a snag with equation (vi). Since the square of every real number is positive or zero, there is no real number whose square is −10; this is a simple example of a quadratic equation with no real roots. The existence of such equations was recognised and accepted for hundreds of years (just as the Greeks had accepted that $x + 10 = 7$ had no solution). Then the 16th century Italians Tartaglia and Cardan found methods of solving cubic and quartic (fourth degree) equations which forced mathematicians to take seriously the square roots of negative numbers. This required a further extension of the number system, to produce what are called *complex numbers*. These were regarded with great suspicion for many years: Descartes called them 'imaginary', Newton called them 'impossible', and Leibniz's mystification has already been quoted. But complex numbers turned out to be very useful, not least in many applications of mathematics, and had become accepted as an essential tool by the time Gauss first gave them a firm logical basis in 1831.

Working with complex numbers

Faced with the problem of wanting the square root of a negative number, we make the following Bold Hypothesis:

> The real number system can be extended by including a new number, denoted by j, which combines with itself and the real numbers according to the usual laws of algebra, but which has the extra property that $j^2 = -1$.

The original notation for j was ι (the Greek letter iota); i is also commonly used instead of j.

The first thing to note is that we do not need further symbols for other square roots. For example, since $-196 = 196 \times (-1) = 14^2 \times j^2$, we see that -196 has the two square roots $\pm 14j$. The following example uses this idea in solving a quadratic equation with no real roots.

EXAMPLE

Solve the equation $z^2 - 6z + 58 = 0$, and check the roots. (We use the letter z for the variable here since we want to keep x and y to stand for *real* numbers.)

Solution

The equation can be rearranged as

$$z^2 - 6z + 9 + 49 = 0$$
$$\Leftrightarrow \quad (z-3)^2 = -49$$
$$\Leftrightarrow \quad z - 3 = \pm 7j$$
$$\Leftrightarrow \quad z = 3 \pm 7j$$

To check:

$$z = 3 + 7j \quad \Rightarrow \quad z^2 - 6z + 58 = (3+7j)^2 - 6(3+7j) + 58$$
$$= 9 + 42j + 49j^2 - 18 - 42j + 58$$
$$= 9 + 42j - 49 - 18 - 42j + 58 \quad (\text{since } j^2 = -1)$$
$$= 0$$

Activity

Check the other root, $z = 3 - 7j$.

A number z of the form $x + yj$, where x and y are real, is called a *complex number*. In the above example we have done some simple calculations with complex numbers; the general methods for addition, subtraction and multiplication are similarly straightforward.

Addition: $(x + yj) + (u + vj) = (x + u) + (y + v)j$

Subtraction: $(x + yj) - (u + vj) = (x - u) + (y - v)j$

Multiplication: $(x + yj)(u + vj) = xu + xvj + yuj + yvj^2$

$$= (xu - yv) + (xv + yu)j \quad (\text{since } j^2 = -1)$$

Division of complex numbers is dealt with in the next section.

Exercise 3A

Express the following in the form $x + yj$.

1. $(8 + 6j) + (6 + 4j)$ **2.** $(9 - 3j) + (-4 + 5j)$ **3.** $(2 + 7j) - (5 + 3j)$

4. $(5 - j) - (6 - 2j)$ **5.** $3(4 + 6j) + 9(1 - 2j)$ **6.** $3j(7 - 4j)$

7. $(9 + 2j)(\frac{1}{6} + \frac{1}{3}j)$ **8.** $(4 - \frac{1}{2}j)(\frac{2}{3} + 2j)$ **9.** $(7 + 3j)^2$

10. $(8 + 6j)(8 - 6j)$ **11.** $(1 + 2j)(3 - 4j)(5 + 6j)$ **12.** $(3 + 2j)^3$

Division of complex numbers

For the complex number $z = x + yj$, x is called the *real part* of the complex number, and y the *imaginary part*, terms introduced by Descartes in 1637. The real and imaginary parts of z are denoted by $\text{Re}(z)$ and $\text{Im}(z)$ respectively, so that, for example, if $z = 3 - 7j$ then $\text{Re}(z) = 3$ and $\text{Im}(z) = -7$. Notice in particular that the imaginary part is real!

Equality of complex numbers is defined in the natural way: the complex numbers $x + yj$ and $u + vj$ are *equal* if $x = u$ and $y = v$.

Before we tackle the slightly more complicated problem of dividing by a complex number, we need a useful further property of equality:

$x + yj = u + vj \quad \Rightarrow \quad x - u = (v - y)j \quad$ (subtracting $u + yj$ from both sides)

$\Rightarrow \quad (x - u)^2 = [(v - y)j]^2 \quad$ (squaring both sides)

$\Rightarrow \quad (x - u)^2 = -(v - y)^2$

But the squares of the real numbers $x - u$ and $v - y$ cannot be negative, so unless both sides of the final equation are zero there is a contradiction. Therefore

$$x + yj = u + vj \quad \Rightarrow \quad x - u = 0 \quad \text{and} \quad v - y = 0$$

$$\Rightarrow \quad x = u \quad \text{and} \quad y = v$$

This shows that equality of real and imaginary parts is a *necessary condition* for equality of complex numbers (as well as being a sufficient condition by definition). When we use this result we say we are *equating real and imaginary parts*.

If you feel that this is making a fuss about something which is obvious, consider the similar question of the equality of rational numbers. It is true that the rational numbers $\frac{x}{y}$ and $\frac{u}{v}$ are equal if $x = u$ and $y = v$, but the converse is not true.

For example, $\frac{3}{2} = \frac{12}{8}$ *but* $3 \neq 12$ *and* $2 \neq 8$.

Equating real and imaginary parts is a very useful method which often yields 'two for the price of one' when working with complex numbers. The following example illustrates this.

EXAMPLE Find real numbers p and q such that $p + qj = \dfrac{1}{3 + 5j}$.

Solution

We have to find real numbers p and q such that

$$(p + qj)(3 + 5j) = 1$$

Expanding gives

$$3p - 5q + (5p + 3q)j = 1$$

Equating real and imaginary parts gives

$$3p - 5q = 1$$

$$5p + 3q = 0$$

These simultaneous equations give $p = \dfrac{3}{34}$, $q = -\dfrac{5}{34}$ and so

$$\frac{1}{3 + 5j} = \frac{3}{34} - \frac{5}{34}j$$

Activity

Prove by a similar method that $\dfrac{1}{x + yj} = \dfrac{x - yj}{x^2 + y^2}$.

Knowing how to find a reciprocal makes other divisions straightforward.

EXAMPLE Find the real and imaginary parts of $\dfrac{7 + 4j}{3 + 5j}$.

Solution

$$\frac{7 + 4j}{3 + 5j} = (7 + 4j) \times \frac{1}{3 + 5j}$$

$$= (7 + 4j) \times \frac{3 - 5j}{34} \quad \text{(using the result of the previous example)}$$

$$= \frac{41 - 23j}{34}$$

so the real part is $\dfrac{41}{34}$, and the imaginary part is $-\dfrac{23}{34}$.

In practice the easiest way to do a division is to note that

$$(x + yj)(x - yj) = x^2 - y^2j^2 = x^2 + y^2$$

which is real.

The complex number $x - yj$ is called the *complex conjugate* (or just the *conjugate*) of $x + yj$; the complex conjugate of z is denoted by z^*. To do a division you start by multiplying the numerator and the denominator by the conjugate of the denominator.

EXAMPLE Express $\dfrac{9 - 4j}{2 + 3j}$ as a complex number.

Solution

$$\frac{9-4j}{2+3j} = \frac{9-4j}{2+3j} \times \frac{2-3j}{2-3j} = \frac{18-27j-8j+12j^2}{2^2+3^2} = \frac{6-35j}{13} = \frac{6}{13} - \frac{35}{13}j$$

The corresponding general result is obtained in the same way:

$$\frac{x+yj}{u+vj} = \frac{(x+yj)(u-vj)}{(u+vj)(u-vj)} = \frac{xu+yv}{u^2+v^2} + \frac{yu-xv}{u^2+v^2}j$$

unless $u = v = 0$, in which case the division is impossible (not surprisingly, since the denominator is then zero).

Cautionary Note: the collapse of a Bold Hypothesis

We have just avoided a mathematical inconvenience (that -1 has no real square root) by introducing a new mathematical object, j, which has the property we want: $j^2 = -1$. What happens if we try the same approach to get rid of the equally inconvenient ban on dividing by zero? The problem is that there is no real number equal to $1 \div 0$. So let us make the Bold Hypothesis that we can introduce a new mathematical object which equals $1 \div 0$ but otherwise behaves like a real number. We shall denote this new object by ∞.

Then $1 \div 0 = \infty$, and so $1 = 0 \times \infty$.

But then we soon meet a contradiction:

$$2 \times 0 = 3 \times 0$$
$$\Rightarrow \quad (2 \times 0) \times \infty = (3 \times 0) \times \infty$$
$$\Rightarrow \quad 2 \times (0 \times \infty) = 3 \times (0 \times \infty)$$
$$\Rightarrow \quad 2 \times 1 = 3 \times 1$$
$$\Rightarrow \quad 2 = 3 \quad \text{which is impossible.}$$

So *this* Bold Hypothesis quickly leads to trouble. How can we be sure that the same will never happen with complex numbers? One way of answering this is given in Pure Mathematics 6; for the moment you will just have to take on trust that there is an answer, and that all is well.

Exercise 3B

Express the complex numbers in Questions 1 – 6 in the form $x + yj$.

1. $\dfrac{1}{3+j}$ **2.** $\dfrac{1}{6-j}$ **3.** $\dfrac{5j}{6-2j}$

4. $\dfrac{7+5j}{6-2j}$ **5.** $\dfrac{47-23j}{6+j}$ **6.** $\dfrac{12-8j}{(2+2j)^2}$

7. (a) Solve the equation $(2+j)(z-7+3j) = 15 - 10j$.

(b) Solve the simultaneous equations

$$3z + 2w = 38$$
$$2z - jw = 7$$

8. Expand and simplify $(a + bj)^3$. Deduce that if $(a + bj)^3$ is real then either $b = 0$ or $b^2 = 3a^2$. Hence find *all* the complex numbers z for which $z^3 = 1$.

9. Simplify (a) j^3; (b) j^4; (c) j^{37}; (d) $\dfrac{1}{j}$; (e) $\dfrac{1}{j^{26}}$. State a general rule for simplifying j^n, where n is any integer.

10. (i) Evaluate (a) $\displaystyle\sum_{r=1}^{100} j^r$; (b) $\displaystyle\sum_{r=-15}^{27} j^r$.

(ii) Find a condition involving the integers p and q which is true if and only if $\displaystyle\sum_{r=p}^{q} j^r = 0$.

11. (i) Expand and simplify $(a + bj)(c + dj)$.

(ii) By equating real and imaginary parts, prove that

$$(a + bj)(c + dj) = 0 \quad \Leftrightarrow \quad a = b = 0 \text{ or } c = d = 0$$

(This shows that, for complex numbers z and w, $zw = 0 \Leftrightarrow z = 0$ or $w = 0$, which is the basis of the method for solving equations by factorising.)

12. Solve
(a) $z^2 + 16 = 0$ (b) $z^2 + 4z + 20 = 0$

(c) $9z^2 - 12z + 29 = 0$ (d) $z^2 - 5jz - 6 = 0$

13. (a) Expand and simplify $(z - \alpha)(z - \beta)$. Deduce that the quadratic equation whose roots are α and β is $z^2 - (\alpha + \beta)z + \alpha\beta = 0$, that is: $z^2 - $ (sum of roots)$z + $ (product of roots) $= 0$.

(b) Find quadratic equations in the form $az^2 + bz + c = 0$ whose roots are

(i) $7 + 4j, 7 - 4j$

(ii) $5j/3, -5j/3$

(iii) $-2 + \sqrt{8}j, -2 - \sqrt{8}j$

(iv) $2 + j, 3 + 2j$

14. Find an example to show that *non-real* numbers p and q may be found such that the equation $z^2 + pz + q = 0$ has a real root. Is it possible for the equation to have two real roots if p and q are non-real?

15. Find real numbers a and b with $a > 0$ such that

(i) $(a + bj)^2 = 21 + 20j$

(ii) $(a + bj)^2 = -40 - 42j$

(iii) $(a + bj)^2 = 1 - 1.875j$

(iv) $(a + bj)^2 = j$

16. Given that $z = 2 + 3j$ is a solution of the equation

$$z^2 + (a - j)z + 16 + bj = 0$$

where a and b are real, find a, b and the other solution of the equation.

17. Solve the equation $z^2 + (-5 + j)z + 6 - 2j = 0$, giving the solutions in the form $x + yj$.

18. Write each expression as a product of linear factors with complex coefficients.

(a) $z^2 + 4$ (b) $z^2 + 6z + 13$ (c) $z^2 + z + 1$ (d) $z^3 + 1$ (e) $z^4 + 1$

[**Hint** for (e): $z^4 + 1 = (z^2 + 1)^2 - 2z^2$.]

19. (i) Evaluate (a) $(1 + j)^2$, (b) $(1 + j)^4$, and (c) $(1 + j)^{4k}$, where k is a positive integer.

(ii) By considering the binominal expansion of $(1 + j)^{4k}$, prove that

$$^{4k}C_0 - {}^{4k}C_2 + {}^{4k}C_4 - {}^{4k}C_6 + \ldots + {}^{4k}C_{4k} = (-4)^k$$

(iii) Check this numerically in the cases (a) $k = 3$, (b) $k = 4$.

(iv) Investigate in a similar way the value of

$$^{4k+2}C_1 - {}^{4k+2}C_3 + {}^{4k+2}C_5 - {}^{4k+2}C_7 + \ldots + {}^{4k+2}C_{4k+1}$$

Representing complex numbers geometrically

Since each complex number $x + yj$ corresponds uniquely to the ordered pair of real numbers (x, y), it is natural to represent $x + yj$ by the point with Cartesian co-ordinates (x, y). For example, in figure 3.1,

$2 + 3j$ is represented by $(2, 3)$

$-5 - 4j$ is represented by $(-5, -4)$

$2j$ is represented by $(0, 2)$

7 is represented by $(7, 0)$

Figure 3.1

All real numbers are represented by points on the x axis, which is therefore called the *real axis*. Pure imaginary numbers (of the form $0 + yj$) give points on the y axis, which is called the *imaginary axis*. It is useful to label these Re and Im respectively. This geometrical interpretation of complex numbers is called the *complex plane* or the *Argand diagram* after Jean-Robert Argand (1768–1822), a self-taught Swiss book-keeper who published an account of it in 1806.

Activity

Copy figure 3.1. For each of the four given points z mark also the point $-z$. Describe the geometrical transformation which maps the point representing z to the point representing $-z$.

Activity

Describe the geometrical transformation which maps the point representing z to the point representing its complex conjugate z^*.

You will have seen in these activities that the points representing z and $-z$ have half-turn symmetry about the origin, and that the points representing z and z^* are reflections of each other in the real axis.

Exercise 3C

In Questions 1 – 6, represent the given complex numbers on the Argand diagram.

1. $3 + 2j$ **2.** $4j$ **3.** $-5 + j$ **4.** -2 **5.** $-6 - 5j$ **6.** $4 - 3j$

7. Given that $z = 2 - 4j$, represent the following by points on the Argand diagram.

(i) z (ii) $-z$ (iii) z^* (iv) $-z^*$ (v) jz (vi) $-jz$ (vii) jz^* (viii) $(jz)^*$

Exercise 3C continued

8. Given that $z = 10 + 5j$ and $w = 1 + 2j$, show the following points on the Argand diagram.

(i) z (ii) w (iii) $z + w$ (iv) $z - w$

(v) $w - z$ (vi) zw (vii) z/w (viii) w/z

9. If $z = 1 + j$, plot the points z^n on a single Argand diagram for $n = -1, 0, 1, 2, 3, 4, 5$. Join each point to its predecessor and to the origin. What do you notice?

10. Give a geometrical proof that $(-z)^* = -z^*$.

Representing complex numbers by vectors

Several mathematicians before Argand had used the complex plane representation. In particular, a Norwegian surveyor, Caspar Wessel (1745 – 1818), wrote a paper in 1797 (largely ignored until it was republished in French a century later) in which the complex number $x + yj$ is represented by the *position vector* $\begin{pmatrix} x \\ y \end{pmatrix}$, figure 3.2. The advantage of this is that the addition of complex numbers can then be shown by the addition of the corresponding vectors. This is because

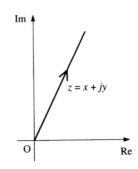

Figure 3.2

$$z_1 + z_2 = (x_1 + x_2) + (y_1 + y_2)j \quad \text{and} \quad \begin{pmatrix} x_1 \\ y_1 \end{pmatrix} + \begin{pmatrix} x_2 \\ y_2 \end{pmatrix} = \begin{pmatrix} x_1 + x_2 \\ y_1 + y_2 \end{pmatrix}$$

so that the procedure of adding x and y components separately is the same in both cases (figure 3.3).

In the Argand diagram the points representing $0, z_1, z_1 + z_2, z_2$ form a parallelogram (figure 3.4).

Figure 3.3

Figure 3.4

We can also represent z by any other directed line segment with components $\begin{pmatrix} x \\ y \end{pmatrix}$, not anchored at the origin as a position vector. Then addition can be shown by a triangle of vectors (figure 3.5).

If we draw the other diagonal of the parallelogram, and let it represent the complex number w (figure 3.6) then

$$z_2 + w = z_1$$
$$\Rightarrow \quad w = z_1 - z_2$$

Figure 3.5

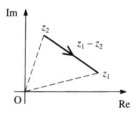

Figure 3.6

This gives a useful illustration of subtraction: the complex number $z_1 - z_2$ is represented by the vector from the point representing z_2 to the point representing z_1, as shown in figure 3.7.

Figure 3.7

NOTE

1. *In figure 3.7 notice*
   (a) *the order of the points: the vector $z_1 - z_2$ goes from the point z_2 to the point z_1;*
   (b) *the simultaneous use of the point and vector representations.*

2. *From now on we omit the words 'representing' or 'represented by', and just say, for example, 'the point $5 + 2j$' or 'the vector $2 - 3j$'.*

Activity

(i) Draw a diagram to illustrate $z_2 - z_1$.

(ii) Draw a diagram to illustrate that $z_1 - z_2 = z_1 + (-z_2)$. Show that this gives the same vector $z_1 - z_2$ as before, but represented by a line segment in a different place.

Having interpreted addition and subtraction in the Argand diagram you may wonder about multiplication and division. A few simple cases are explored in Questions 1 and 2 of Exercise 3D, but the full story is best left until a little later (page 78): it is worth waiting for!

Exercise 3D

1. (i) If $z = 2 + 3j$, plot the points kz on a single Argand diagram for $k = -2, -1, -\frac{1}{4}, 0, \frac{1}{2}, 1, 3$.

   (ii) Repeat part (i) with a different z of your choice and a different set of real values of k.

   (iii) What is the relation between the points z and kz, where k is real?

2. (i) If $z = -4 + 2j$, represent the points z and jz by position vectors on a single diagram.

   (ii) Repeat part (i) for two other complex numbers z of your choice.

   (iii) What is the relation between the vectors z and jz?

   (iv) Explain how the geometrical interpretation of multiplication by j which you have given in part (iii) fits with the statement $j^2 = -1$.

   [**Hint:** Multiplying by j^2 means multiplying by j twice.]

3. The figure below consists of five squares on the Argand diagram. One vertex represents the number z, as shown. Copy the figure, and label each vertex with the complex number it represents.

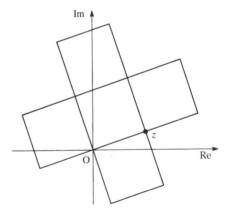

4. Prove that the point $\frac{1}{2}(z_1 + z_2)$ is halfway between the points z_1 and z_2.

5. In an Argand diagram the points A, B, C, D represent the complex numbers a, b, c, d respectively. Write down the vectors $\overrightarrow{AB}$ and $\overrightarrow{DC}$ in terms of a, b, c, d. Hence show that

$$\text{ABCD is a parallelogram} \iff a + c = b + d$$

   [Note: the term 'parallelogram' is here taken to include certain 'collapsed' cases, which you would not usually describe as parallelograms; you should identify these.]

6. If the points $2 - 3j, -1 - j, -3 + 4j$ are three vertices of a parallelogram, find all the possible fourth vertices. Draw all these parallelograms on a single Argand diagram.

Exercise 3D continued

7. The points $6 + j$, $-2 + 5j$ are the opposite vertices of a square. Find the centre of the square and the vector from the centre to $6 + j$. Use Question 2 (iii) to find the other two vertices of the square.

8. Two vertices of a square are $7 + 2j$ and $3 - 6j$. Find the other vertices

  (i) when the given points are opposite vertices;

  (ii) when the given points are adjacent vertices, dealing with both possible squares.

The modulus of a complex number

The distance of the point representing z from the origin is called the *modulus* of z, and is denoted by $|z|$. Thus

$$z = x + yj \quad \Rightarrow \quad |z| = \sqrt{(x^2 + y^2)}$$

If z is real, $z = x$ say, then $|z| = \sqrt{(x^2)}$, which is the absolute value of x, i.e. $|x|$. So the use of the modulus sign with complex numbers fits with its previous meaning for real numbers.

Sets of points in the Argand diagram

When z is represented by a vector, $|z|$ means the length of that vector. Since the vector $z_1 - z_2$ goes from the point z_2 to the point z_1 it follows that $|z_1 - z_2|$ is the distance between the points z_1 and z_2.

This is the key to solving many questions about sets of points in the Argand diagram, as in the following examples.

EXAMPLE

Draw an Argand diagram showing the set of points z for which $|z - 3 - 4j| = 5$.

Solution

$|z - 3 - 4j|$ can be written as $|z - (3 + 4j)|$, and this is the distance from the point $3 + 4j$ to the point z. This will equal 5 if and only if the point z lies on the circle with centre $3 + 4j$ and radius 5 (see diagram).

EXAMPLE Draw an Argand diagram showing the set of points z for which
$|z - 3 - 4j| \leqslant |z + 1 - 2j|$.

Solution

$|z - 3 - 4j|$ is the distance from the point
$3 + 4j$ (A say) to the point z as in the
previous example, and

$$|z + 1 - 2j| = |z - (-1 + 2j)|$$

is the distance from the point $-1 + 2j$
(B say) to the point z. These distances
are equal if and only if z is on the
perpendicular bisector of AB. The given
condition holds if and only if z is on this
bisector or in the half plane on the side of it
containing A (shaded in diagram).

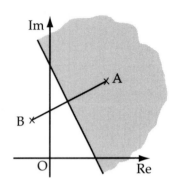

Exercise 3E

In Questions 1 – 7, draw an Argand diagram showing the set of points z for which the given condition is true.

1. $|z| = 2$ **2.** $|z - 4| \leqslant 3$ **3.** $|z - 5j| = 6$ **4.** $|z + 3 - 4j| < 5$

5. $|6 - j - z| \geqslant 2$ **6.** $|z + 2 + 4j| = 0$ **7.** $2 \leqslant |z - 1 + j| \leqslant 3$

8. Draw an Argand diagram showing the set of points z for which $|z - 12 + 5j| \leqslant 7$. Use the diagram to prove that, for these z, $6 \leqslant |z| \leqslant 20$.

9. What are the greatest and least values of $|z + 3 - 2j|$ if $|z - 5 + 4j| \leqslant 3$?

10. By using an Argand diagram see if it is possible to find values of z for which $|z - 2 + j| \geqslant 10$ and $|z + 4 + 2j| \leqslant 2$ simultaneously.

In Questions 11 – 18, draw an Argand diagram showing the set of points z for which the given condition is true.

11. $|z| = |z - 4|$ **12.** $|z| \geqslant |z - 2j|$ **13.** $\text{Re}(z) = -2$

14. $|z + 1 - j| = |z - 1 + j|$ **15.** $\text{Im}(z + 3 - 5j) < 0$ **16.** $|z + 5 + 7j| \leqslant |z - 2 - 6j|$

17. $|z + 8 + 2j| = |z - 6 + 2j| = |z - 4 - 4j|$ **18.** $|z + 8 + 2j| \leqslant |z - 6 + 2j| \leqslant |z - 4 - 4j|$

19. (i) Prove that if $|a| = |b|$ then the general point on the line through the point p perpendicular to the line joining points a and b can be written as $p + t(a + b)$, where t is real.

    (ii) ABCD is a cyclic quadrilateral. Through the mid-point of each side or diagonal a line is drawn perpendicular to the opposite side or other diagonal. Prove that these six lines meet at a single point.

Some properties of conjugates

First a reminder about notation. The conjugate of the complex number z is denoted by z^*, so that if $z = x + yj$ then $z^* = x - yj$, and the real and imaginary parts of z are denoted by Re (z) and Im (z) respectively.

Conjugates have the following properties.

1. $(z^*)^* = z$
2. $(z_1 + z_2)^* = z_1^* + z_2^*$
3. $(z_1 - z_2)^* = z_1^* - z_2^*$
4. $(z_1 z_2)^* = z_1^* z_2^*$
5. $(z_1/z_2)^* = z_1^*/z_2^*$
6. Re $(z) = (z + z^*)/2$, Im $(z) = (z - z^*)/2j$

All these properties can be proved directly from the definitions. For example, to prove (4), let $z_1 = x_1 + y_1 j$ and $z_2 = x_2 + y_2 j$. Then

$$z_1 z_2 = (x_1 + y_1 j)(x_2 + y_2 j)$$
$$= (x_1 x_2 - y_1 y_2) + (x_1 y_2 + x_2 y_1)j$$
$$(z_1 z_2)^* = (x_1 x_2 - y_1 y_2) - (x_1 y_2 + x_2 y_1)j$$
$$= (x_1 - y_1 j)(x_2 - y_2 j)$$
$$= z_1^* z_2^*$$

Activity

Prove the other properties in a similar way.

NOTE

You may have found that to prove property (5) in this way is rather tedious; it is more elegant to make use of (4) to prove (5), as follows.

Let $w = z_1/z_2$, so that $wz_2 = z_1$. Then $w^* z_2^* = z_1^*$ by (4), so that $w^* = z_1^*/z_2^*$, which proves (5).

Activity

Use property (4) to prove by induction that $(z^n)^* = (z^*)^n$.

There is a useful link between the conjugate and the modulus of a complex number: since $|z|^2 = x^2 + y^2 = (x + yj)(x - yj)$ it follows that $|z|^2 = zz^*$.

This in turn leads to the further properties:

7. $|z_1 z_2| = |z_1||z_2|$
8. $|z_1/z_2| = |z_1|/|z_2|$

Activity

Use properties of conjugates to prove properties (7) and (8).

Exercise 3F

1. Given that $z = 2 + 3j$ and $w = 6 - 4j$, find

(i) $\text{Re}(z)$ (ii) $\text{Im}(w)$ (iii) $z^* + w^*$ (iv) $\text{Im}(z + z^*)$

(v) $(z^3)^*$ (vi) $(z^*)^3$ (vii) $zw^* - z^*w$

2. Given that $z = x + yj$ find $\dfrac{1}{z} + \dfrac{1}{z^*}$ in terms of x and y.

3. Prove that $1/(\cos\theta + j\sin\theta) = \cos\theta - j\sin\theta$.

4. (i) Use the properties of conjugates to prove that $z^n - (z^*)^n$ is pure imaginary (i.e. has zero real part).

(ii) Simplify $(1 + j)^{-3} - (1 - j)^{-3}$.

5. (i) Simplify $(zw^*)^*$.

(ii) Use conjugates to prove that $zw^* + z^*w$ is real and that $zw^* - z^*w$ is pure imaginary.

6. (i) Work out and simplify $(5 + 4j)^3$, and hence write down the simplified form of $(5 - 4j)^3$.

(ii) Noting that $41 = 5^2 + 4^2 = (5 + 4j)(5 - 4j)$, use the result from part (i) to express 41^3 as the sum of two squares.

7. Find all the complex numbers z for which

8. Use conjugates to prove that $|z - w|^2 + |z + w|^2 = 2|z|^2 + 2|w|^2$.

Deduce that the sum of the squares of the sides of a parallelogram equals the sum of the squares of its diagonals.

9. By representing z_1, z_2 and $z_1 + z_2$ as vectors, show that $|z_1 + z_2| \leqslant |z_1| + |z_2|$, and explain when equality occurs. Prove similarly that $|z_1 + z_2| \geqslant ||z_1| - |z_2||$. Verify these inequalities in the case $z_1 = 7 + 12j$, $z_2 = 5 + 7j$. (These are called the *triangle inequalities*.)

10. If $z = 12 - 9j$ and $|w| = 5$, find w

(i) when $|z + w| = |z| + |w|$;

(ii) when $|z + w| = |z| - |w|$.

11. Verify that $(c - a)(d - b) = (b - a)(d - c) + (d - a)(c - b)$. Use a triangle inequality to deduce that if A, B, C, D are any four points in a plane then

$$\text{AC} \times \text{BD} \leqslant \text{AB} \times \text{CD} + \text{AD} \times \text{BC}$$

Complex numbers and equations

The reason for inventing complex numbers was to provide solutions for quadratic equations which have no real root, i.e. to solve $az^2 + bz + c = 0$ when the discriminant $b^2 - 4ac$ is negative. This is straightforward since if $b^2 - 4ac = -k^2$ (where k is real) then the formula for solving quadratic equations gives $z = \dfrac{-b \pm kj}{2a}$; these are the two complex roots of the equation. Notice that these roots are *conjugate* complex numbers.

It would be natural to think that to solve cubic equations would require a further extension of the number system to give some sort of 'super-complex' numbers, with ever more extensions to deal with higher degree equations. But luckily things are much simpler: it turns out that *all* polynomial equations (even those with complex coefficients) can be solved by means of complex numbers. This was realised as early as 1629 by Albert Girard, who stated that an nth degree polynomial equation has precisely n roots, including complex roots and taking into account repeated roots. (For example, the fifth degree equation $(z - 2)(z - 4)^2(z^2 + 9) = 0$ has the five roots 2, 4 (twice), $3j$, $-3j$.) Many great mathematicians tried to prove this. The chief difficulty is to show that every polynomial equation must have at least *one* root: this is called the *Fundamental Theorem of Algebra*, and was first proved by Gauss (again!) in 1799.

The Fundamental Theorem (which is too difficult to prove here) is an example of an *existence theorem*: it tells us that a solution exists, but does not say what it is. To find the solutions of a particular equation we may be able to use an exact method such as the formula for the roots of a quadratic equation (there are much more complicated formulae for solving cubic or quartic equations, but not in general for equations of degree five or more). Alternatively there are good approximate methods for finding roots to any required accuracy – you may have access to a computer system or calculator with this facility.

Activity

If so, find out how to use it.

We have already noted that the complex roots of a quadratic equation occur as a conjugate pair. The same is true of the complex roots of any polynomial equation with real coefficients. This can be proved by using the properties of conjugates you met in the previous section, as follows.

Let $P(z) = c_0z^n + c_1z^{n-1} + c_2z^{n-2} + \dots + c_n$ be a polynomial with *real* coefficients c_r. Then

$$\begin{aligned}(P(z))^* &= (c_0z^n)^* + (c_1z^{n-1})^* + (c_2z^{n-2})^* + \dots + c_n^* &&\text{(by property (2), page 69)}\\ &= c_0^*(z^n)^* + c_1^*(z^{n-1})^* + c_2^*(z^{n-2})^* + \dots + c_n^* &&\text{(by property (4))}\\ &= c_0(z^n)^* + c_1(z^{n-1})^* + c_2(z^{n-2})^* + \dots + c_n &&\text{(since the } c_r \text{ are real)}\\ &= c_0(z^*)^n + c_1(z^*)^{n-1} + c_2(z^*)^{n-2} + \dots + c_n &&\text{(since } (z^r)^* = (z^*)^r)\\ &= P(z^*).\end{aligned}$$

Therefore α is a root of $P(z) = 0 \quad \Leftrightarrow \quad P(\alpha) = 0$

$$\Leftrightarrow \quad P(\alpha^*) = (P(\alpha))^* = 0^* = 0$$

$$\Leftrightarrow \quad \alpha^* \text{ is a root of } P(z) = 0.$$

This shows that the complex roots of a polynomial equation with real coefficients occur in conjugate pairs: α is a root if and only if α^* is a root.

Activity

Show that the equation $z^2 - 3jz - 2 = 0$ has roots j and $2j$, which are *not* conjugate. (This emphasises that the equation must have *real* coefficients for the theorem to hold.)

EXAMPLE

Given that $1 + 2j$ is a root of $4z^3 - 11z^2 + 26z - 15 = 0$, find the other roots.

Solution

Since the coefficients are real, the conjugate $1 - 2j$ is also a root.

Therefore the polynomial $4z^3 - 11z^2 + 26z - 15$ has

$$\begin{aligned}[z - (1 + 2j)][z - (1 - 2j)] &= [(z - 1) - 2j][(z - 1) + 2j]\\ &= (z - 1)^2 + 4\\ &= z^2 - 2z + 5 \text{ as a factor.}\end{aligned}$$

By looking at the coefficient of z^3 and the constant term we can easily see that the remaining factor is $4z - 3$, and hence that the third root is $\frac{3}{4}$.

Exercise 3G

1. Check that $2 + j$ is a root of $z^3 - z^2 - 7z + 15 = 0$, and find the other roots.

2. One root of $z^3 - 15z^2 + 76z - 140 = 0$ is an integer. Solve the equation.

3. Given that $1 - j$ is a root of $z^3 + pz^2 + qz + 12 = 0$, find the real numbers p and q, and the other roots.

4. One root of $z^4 - 10z^3 + 42z^2 - 82z + 65 = 0$ is $3 + 2j$. Solve the equation.

Exercise 3G continued

5. The equation $z^4 - 8z^3 + 20z^2 - 72z + 99 = 0$ has a pure imaginary root. Solve the equation.

6. (i) Express $P(z) \equiv (z^2 + 25)(z^2 + 6z + 10)$ in the form
$(z - \alpha)(z - \alpha^*)(z - \beta)(z - \beta^*)$.

(ii) Find real polynomials $U(z)$ and $V(z)$ such that
$(z - \alpha)(z - \beta) \equiv U(z) + jV(z)$, and write down $(z - \alpha^*)(z - \beta^*)$ in a similar form.

(iii) Hence show that $P(z) \equiv [U(z)]^2 + [V(z)]^2$.

[A *real* polynomial is a polynomial with real coefficients.]

7. (i) Suppose that $h = a^2 + b^2$ and $k = c^2 + d^2$, where a, b, c, d are integers. Express hk as the sum of two perfect squares.
[**Hint**: Use complex factors and conjugates.]

(ii) Prove by induction that if h can be expressed as the sum of two perfect squares then so can h^n for every positive integer n.

8. Generalise the method of Question 6 to prove that any real polynomial $P(z)$ which is positive for all real values of z can be expressed as the sum of the squares of two real polynomials.

The polar form of complex numbers

The position vector of the point z in the Argand diagram can be described by means of its length r and the angle θ it makes with the positive real axis (figure 3.8).

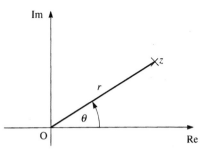

Figure 3.8

The distance r is of course $|z|$, the modulus of z as defined on page 67. The angle θ is slightly more complicated: it is measured anticlockwise from the positive real axis, normally in radians, but is not uniquely defined since adding $2k\pi$ (for any integer k) to θ gives the same direction. To avoid confusion, it is usual to choose that value of θ for which $-\pi < \theta \leqslant \pi$; this is called the *principal argument* of z, denoted by arg z. Then every complex number except 0 has a unique principal argument: the argument of 0 is undefined. For example, with reference to figure 3.9,

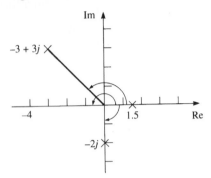

$$\arg(-4) = \pi$$
$$\arg(-2j) = -\pi/2$$
$$\arg(1.5) = 0$$
$$\arg(-3 + 3j) = 3\pi/4$$

Figure 3.9

Activity

Find (i) arg j; (ii) arg $(\sqrt{3} + j)$; (iii) arg$(-4 - 4j)$; (iv) arg $[(-1 - \sqrt{3}j)/2]$.

It is clear from figure 3.10 that

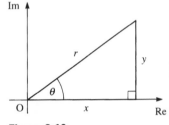

$$x = r\cos\theta \qquad y = r\sin\theta$$
$$r = \sqrt{(x^2 + y^2)} \quad \tan\theta = y/x$$

and the same relations hold in the other quadrants too.

Figure 3.10

These can be used to find the real and imaginary parts from the modulus and argument, and vice versa, but care is needed in finding the argument from the real and imaginary parts. It is tempting to say that $\theta = \arctan(y/x)$, but this gives a value between $-\pi/2$ and $\pi/2$, which is correct only if z is in the first or fourth quadrants. For example, the point $z_1 = 2 - 3j$ is in the fourth quadrant, and its argument is correctly given by arctan $(-3/2) \approx -0.98$ rad $(\approx -56°)$. But $z_2 = -2 + 3j$ is in the second quadrant, where its argument is arctan $(3/-2) + \pi \approx 2.16$ rad $(\approx 124°)$ as in figure 3.11.

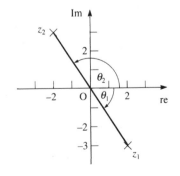

Figure 3.11

The general results for all quadrants are shown in figure 3.12. It is wise to draw a sketch diagram each time.

$\arg z = \arctan(y/x) + \pi$	$\arg z = \arctan(y/x)$
$\arg z = \arctan(y/x) - \pi$	$\arg z = \arctan(y/x)$

Figure 3.12

Activity

Mark the points $1 + j$, $1 - j$, $-1 + j$, $-1 - j$ on an Argand diagram. Find $\arg z$ for each of these, and check that the statements in figure 3.12 are correct.

Activity

Most calculators can convert from (x,y) to (r,θ) (called *rectangular* to *polar*, and often shown as $R \rightarrow P$) and from (r,θ) to (x,y) (polar to rectangular, $P \rightarrow R$). Find how to use these facilities on your calculator, and compare with other available types of calculator. Does your calculator always give the correct θ, or do you sometimes have to add or subtract π?

Since $x = r\cos\theta$ and $y = r\sin\theta$ we can write the complex number $z = x + yj$ in the form

$$z = r(\cos\theta + j\sin\theta)$$

This is called the *polar* or *modulus–argument* form. For example

$$-1 + j = \sqrt{2}[\cos(3\pi/4) + j\sin(3\pi/4)]$$

$$7j = 7[\cos(\pi/2) + j\sin(\pi/2)]$$

$$-3 = 3(\cos\pi + j\sin\pi)$$

$$4 + 3j = 5(\cos\alpha + j\sin\alpha) \quad \text{where } \alpha = \arctan(3/4) \approx 0.644$$

Exercise 3H

In Questions 1 – 16, find the modulus and principal argument. Give the argument in radians, either as a simple rational multiple of π or correct to three decimal places.

1. 1 **2.** -2 **3.** $3j$ **4.** $-4j$ **5.** $1 + j$ **6.** $-5 - 5j$ **7.** $1 - \sqrt{3}j$

8. $6\sqrt{3} + 6j$ **9.** $-\sqrt{18} + \sqrt{18}j$ **10.** $8[\cos(\pi/5) + j\sin(\pi/5)]$

11. $(\cos 2.3 + j\sin 2.3)/4$ **12.** $-3[\cos(-3) + j\sin(-3)]$

13. $3 - 4j$ **14.** $-12 + 5j$ **15.** $4 + 7j$ **16.** $-58 - 93j$

Exercise 3H continued

17. Given that $\arg(5 + 2j) = \alpha$, find the principal argument of each of the following in terms of α.

　　(i) $-5 - 2j$　　(ii) $5 - 2j$　　(iii) $-5 + 2j$　　(iv) $2 + 5j$　　(v) $-2 + 5j$

In Questions 18 – 22, write the complex numbers in polar form.

18. $\cos\alpha - j\sin\alpha$　　　　**19.** $3(\sin\alpha + j\cos\alpha)$　　　　**20.** $j(\cos\alpha + j\sin\alpha)$

21. $10/(\cos\alpha + j\sin\alpha)$　　　　**22.** $1 + j\tan\alpha$

23. (i) Given that $z = \cos\theta + j\sin\theta$, plot the points $0, 1, z, 1 + z$ on an Argand diagram. What sort of quadrilateral do these points form? Hence find the modulus and argument of $1 + \cos\theta + j\sin\theta$.

　　(ii) Obtain the same result by expressing $1 + \cos\theta + j\sin\theta$ in terms of $\cos(\theta/2)$ and $\sin(\theta/2)$.

　　(iii) Find the modulus and argument of $1 - \cos\theta - j\sin\theta$.

Sets of points using the polar form

EXAMPLE

Draw Argand diagrams showing the sets of points z for which

(i) $\arg z = \pi/4$　　　　　　　　　(ii) $\arg(z - j) = \pi/4$

(iii) $0 \leqslant \arg(z - j) \leqslant \pi/4$　　　　(iv) $\arg(z - j) = \arg(z - 2 + j)$

Solution

(i)　$\arg z = \pi/4$

　　$\Leftrightarrow$ the vector z has direction $\pi/4$

　　$\Leftrightarrow$ z lies on the half-line from the origin in the $\pi/4$ direction.

　　(Note that the origin is not included, since arg 0 is undefined.)

(ii)　$\arg(z - j) = \pi/4$

　　$\Leftrightarrow$ the vector $z - j$ from the point j to the point z has direction $\pi/4$

　　$\Leftrightarrow$ z lies on the half-line from the point j in the $\pi/4$ direction.

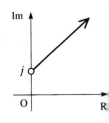

(iii)　$0 \leqslant \arg(z - j) \leqslant \pi/4$

　　$\Leftrightarrow$ the vector $z - j$ from the point j to the point z has direction between 0 and $\pi/4$ (inclusive)

　　$\Leftrightarrow$ z lies in the one-eighth plane shown in the diagram.

(iv) $\arg(z-j) = \arg(z-2+j)$

  $\Leftrightarrow$ the vectors from points j and $2-j$ to the point z are in the same direction and sense

  $\Leftrightarrow$ z lies on the line joining points j and $2-j$, but does not lie between these points or at either of them.

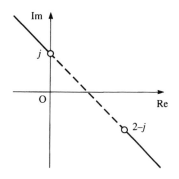

Exercise 3I

In Questions 1 – 6, draw an Argand diagram showing the set of points z for which the given condition is true.

1. $\arg z = -\pi/3$　**2.** $\arg(z-4j) = 0$　**3.** $\arg(z+3) \geqslant \pi/2$　**4.** $\arg(z+1+2j) = 3\pi/4$

5. $\arg(z-3+j) \leqslant -\pi/6$　**6.** $-\pi/4 \leqslant \arg(z+5-3j) \leqslant \pi/3$

7. Find the least and greatest possible values of $\arg z$ if $|z-8j| \leqslant 4$.

8. If k is positive and $|z| \leqslant k$, prove that $0 \leqslant |z+k| \leqslant 2k$ and $-\pi/2 < \arg(z+k) < \pi/2$. Find the least and greatest values of $|z+2k|$ and $\arg(z+2k)$.

In Questions 9 – 11, draw an Argand diagram showing the set of points z for which the condition is true.

9. $\arg z = \arg(z+2)$　**10.** $\arg(z-2-5j) = \arg(z+4-2j)$

11. $\arg(z+j) = \arg(z-3) + \pi$.

12. Prove that the set of points for which $\arg(z-1) = \arg(z+1) + \pi/4$ is part of the set of points for which $|z-j| = \sqrt{2}$, and show which part clearly in a diagram.

Multiplication in the Argand diagram

The polar form quickly leads to an elegant geometrical interpretation of the multiplication of complex numbers. For if

$$z_1 = r_1(\cos\theta_1 + j\sin\theta_1) \quad \text{and} \quad z_2 = r_2(\cos\theta_2 + j\sin\theta_2)$$

then

$$z_1 z_2 = r_1 r_2(\cos\theta_1 + j\sin\theta_1)(\cos\theta_2 + j\sin\theta_2)$$

$$= r_1 r_2[\cos\theta_1\cos\theta_2 - \sin\theta_1\sin\theta_2 + j(\sin\theta_1\cos\theta_2 + \cos\theta_1\sin\theta_2)]$$

Using the compound angle formulae gives

$$z_1 z_2 = r_1 r_2[\cos(\theta_1 + \theta_2) + j\sin(\theta_1 + \theta_2)]$$

This is the complex number with modulus $r_1 r_2$ and argument $(\theta_1 + \theta_2)$, so we have the beautiful result that

$$|z_1 z_2| = |z_1|\,|z_2|$$

and

$$\arg(z_1 z_2) = \arg z_1 + \arg z_2 \quad (\pm 2\pi \text{ if necessary,}$$

to give the principal argument)

So to multiply complex numbers in polar form we *multiply* their moduli and *add* their arguments.

Activity

Using this interpretation, investigate (i) multiplication by j; (ii) multiplication by -1.

This gives the following simple geometrical interpretation of multiplication.

To obtain the vector $z_1 z_2$, enlarge the vector z_1 by the scale factor $|z_2|$ and rotate it through $\arg z_2$ anticlockwise about O (figure 3.13).

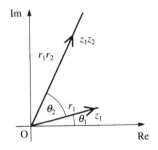

Figure 3.13

This combination of an enlargement followed by a rotation is called a *spiral dilatation*.

Activity

Check this by accurate drawing and measurement for the case $z_1 = 2 + j$, $z_2 = 3 + 4j$. Then do the same with z_1 and z_2 interchanged.

The corresponding results for division are easily obtained by letting $z_1/z_2 = w$. Then $z_1 = w\, z_2$ so that

$$|z_1| = |w|\,|z_2| \quad \text{and} \quad \arg z_1 = \arg w + \arg z_2 \quad (\pm 2\pi \text{ if necessary})$$

Therefore
$$|w| = |z_1/z_2| = |z_1|/|z_2|$$

and

$$\arg w = \arg (z_1/z_2)$$
$$= \arg z_1 - \arg z_2 \quad (\pm 2\pi \text{ if necessary,}$$
$$\text{to give the principal argument)}$$

So to divide complex numbers in polar form we *divide* their moduli and *subtract* their arguments.

Exercise 3J

In Questions 1 – 9, given that $z = 2[\cos(\pi/4) + j\sin(\pi/4)]$ and $w = 3[\cos(\pi/3) + j\sin(\pi/3)]$, find the following in polar form.

1. wz **2.** w/z **3.** z/w **4.** $1/z$ **5.** w^2

6. z^5 **7.** $w^3 z^4$ **8.** $5jz$ **9.** $(1 + j)w$

10. Prove that, in general, $\arg(1/z) = -\arg z$, and deal with the exceptions.

11. Given the points 1 and z on the Argand diagram, explain how to find the following points by geometrical construction:

(i) $3z$ (ii) $2jz$ (iii) $(3 + 2j)z$ (iv) z^* (v) $|z|$ (vi) z^2

12. Describe the motion of each of the points in Question 11 as the point z moves

(i) along the imaginary axis from $-j$ to j;

(ii) once anticlockwise around the circle $|z| = 1$, starting at $z = 1$.

13. By considering powers of $2 + j$, show that the position vector $\begin{pmatrix} 3 \\ 4 \end{pmatrix}$

bisects the angle formed by the position vectors $\begin{pmatrix} 2 \\ 1 \end{pmatrix}$ and $\begin{pmatrix} 2 \\ 11 \end{pmatrix}$.

Check this by vector methods, using the scalar product.

14. Find the real and imaginary parts of $\dfrac{-1+j}{1+\sqrt{3}j}$. Express $-1 + j$ and

$1 + \sqrt{3}j$ in polar form. Hence show that $\cos(5\pi/12) = \dfrac{\sqrt{3}-1}{2\sqrt{2}}$, and find an exact expression for $\sin(5\pi/12)$.

3

Exercise 3J continued

15. The right-hand diagram below shows what happens to the character drawn on the Argand diagram on the left when each point representing z is replaced by the point representing z^2. Explain why

(i) the knife has moved nearer the origin, but got longer;

(ii) his forearm has moved from vertical to horizontal;

(iii) his boots have grown more than his head;

(iv) he has stabbed himself in the stomach.

KEY POINTS

- Complex numbers are of the form $z = x + yj$ with $j^2 = -1$.

- The *conjugate* of z is $z^* = x - yj$.

- Addition and subtraction:

$$(x_1 + y_1 j) \pm (x_2 + y_2 j) = (x_1 \pm x_2) + (y_1 \pm y_2)j$$

- Multiplication:

$$(x_1 + y_1 j)(x_2 + y_2 j) = (x_1 x_2 - y_1 y_2) + (x_1 y_2 + x_2 y_1)j$$

- Division – multiply top and bottom by the conjugate of the bottom:

$$\frac{x_1 + y_1 j}{x_2 + y_2 j} = \frac{(x_1 x_2 + y_1 y_2) + (x_2 y_1 - x_1 y_2)j}{x_2^2 + y_2^2}$$

- The complex number z can be represented geometrically as the point (x, y) [Argand] or the vector $\begin{pmatrix} x \\ y \end{pmatrix}$ [Wessel].

- The modulus of $z = x + yj$ is $|z| = \sqrt{x^2 + y^2}$; this is the distance of the point z from the origin, or the length of the vector z.

- The distance between the points z_1 and z_2 in the Argand diagram is $|z_1 - z_2|$.

- Modulus properties:

$$|z|^2 = zz^* \qquad |z_1 + z_2| \leqslant |z_1| + |z_2|$$

$$|z_1 z_2| = |z_1||z_2| \qquad \left| \frac{z_1}{z_2} \right| = \frac{|z_1|}{|z_2|}$$

- The *principal argument* of z is the angle θ, $-\pi < \theta \leqslant \pi$, such that $\cos\theta : \sin\theta : 1 = x : y : r$, where $r = |z|$.

- The *polar form* of z is $z = r(\cos\theta + j\sin\theta)$.

- Multiplication in polar form – multiplying the moduli, add the arguments:

$$z_1 z_2 = r_1 r_2 [\cos(\theta_1 + \theta_2) + j\sin(\theta_1 + \theta_2)]$$

- Division in polar form – divide the moduli, subtract the arguments:

$$\frac{z_1}{z_2} = \frac{r_1}{r_2} [\cos(\theta_1 - \theta_2) + j\sin(\theta_1 - \theta_2)]$$

4

Matrices

As for everything else, so for a mathematical theory – beauty can be perceived but not explained

Arthur Cayley, 1883

Figure 4.1 shows a pack of cards. Initially the cards are piled up neatly forming a cuboid, but two other arrangements are shown.

Figure 4.1

For Discussion

Describe what has happened in words. Can you suggest ways of representing this symbolically?

In this chapter you will learn about matrices, and how they give you the ability to use algebraic techniques in geometrical and other situations. Matrices are often (but not always) used when creating effects on TV – particularly when the picture is rotated, flipped, enlarged or reduced.

Transformations

In figures 4.2 you will see the effect of various transformations on a standard object. Our standard object includes what is known as the *unit square*, the square with vertices at $(0, 0)$, $(1, 0)$, $(1, 1)$ and $(0, 1)$. In each diagram the point $P'(x', y')$ is the image of $P(x, y)$, and we give the equations connecting x' and y' with x and y. The position and scales of the co-ordinate axes are not changed by the various transformations.

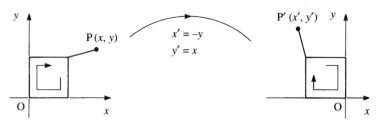

Rotation 90° anticlockwise about O

Reflection in the line $y = x$

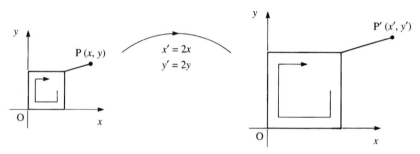

Enlargement, scale factor 2, centre O

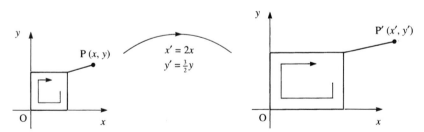

Two-way stretch: $\times 2$ horizontally, $\times \frac{3}{2}$ vertically

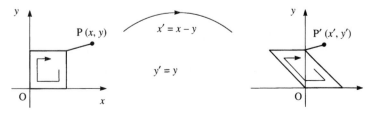

Shear parallel to the x-axis

Figure 4.2

Although these transformations cause different changes of shape, size, location, and *sense* (indicated by the arrow inside the unit square reversing from pointing clockwise to pointing anticlockwise) they have similarities. In these examples:

- the image of the unit square is always a parallelogram – rectangles and squares are examples of parallelograms;

- the vertex O of the unit square has not moved.

A further property of these examples is that the co-ordinates of P' can always be found from the co-ordinates of P using equations of the form

$$\begin{cases} x'= ax + cy \\ y'= bx + dy \end{cases}$$

where a, b, c, d are constants.

We shall summarise a pair of equations like these by just noting the array of coefficients: $\begin{pmatrix} a & c \\ b & d \end{pmatrix}$. This array is called the *matrix* of the transformation.

For example, in the two-way stretch, $a = 2, b = 0, c = 0, d = \frac{3}{2}$, and the matrix is $\begin{pmatrix} 2 & 0 \\ 0 & \frac{3}{2} \end{pmatrix}$.

As the shear shown in figure 4.2 is described by the equations $\begin{cases} x'= 1x - 1y \\ y'= 0x + 1y \end{cases}$ its matrix is $\begin{pmatrix} 1 & -1 \\ 0 & 1 \end{pmatrix}$.

Activity

Write down the matrices which represent

(a) rotation 90° anticlockwise about O;

(b) reflection in the line $y = x$;

(c) enlargement, scale factor 2, centre O.

The example which follows shows how you may prove that a transformation may be represented by a matrix in the way we have described. It also establishes an important general result about rotations.

EXAMPLE The diagram shows a flag and its image following rotation through angle θ anticlockwise about the origin. The image of the point $P(x, y)$ is $P'(x', y')$. Find x' and y' in terms of x, y, and θ, and so find the matrix for this rotation.

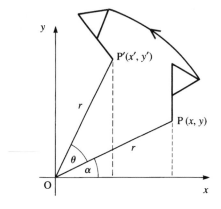

Solution

Let OP be of length r.

Rotate OP through angle θ anticlockwise about O. Then

$$x' = r \cos(\alpha + \theta) = r \cos \alpha \cos \theta - r \sin \alpha \sin \theta$$

$$= x \cos \theta - y \sin \theta$$

$$\text{since } x = r \cos \alpha, y = r \sin \alpha$$

Similarly $\qquad y' = r \sin(\alpha + \theta) = r \sin \alpha \cos \theta + r \cos \alpha \sin \theta$

$$= x \sin \theta + y \cos \theta$$

Thus $\quad x' = x \cos \theta - y \sin \theta$

$\qquad y' = x \sin \theta + y \cos \theta$

and $\begin{pmatrix} \cos \theta & -\sin \theta \\ \sin \theta & \cos \theta \end{pmatrix}$ is the matrix representing a rotation through angle θ anticlockwise about the origin.

Straight lines

Our diagrams have shown the images of straight lines as straight lines. You should assume that any transformation which can be represented by a matrix transforms straight lines into straight lines. (We shall prove that this assumption is correct later.) Thus to find the image of the line l through points A and B, find the image A' of A and the image B' of B; then the image of l is the line through A' and B'.

Activity

A transformation (an example of a *shear*) maps points as follows:

    each point is moved parallel to the x axis;

    each point is moved twice its distance from the x axis;

    points above the x axis are moved to the right;

    points below the x axis are moved to the left.

Pure Mathematics 4

Activity continued

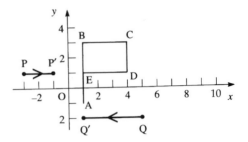

The diagram shows a flag, and points P and Q and their images P′ and Q′.

(i)   Copy the diagram and draw the image of the flag.

(ii)   Show that the image of (x, y) is the point $(x + 2y, y)$ and find the matrix which represents this transformation.

The origin does not move

Notice that substituting $x = 0$ and $y = 0$ into $\begin{cases} x' = ax + cy \\ y' = bx + dy \end{cases}$ gives $\begin{cases} x' = 0 \\ y' = 0 \end{cases}$.

This means that whenever we can represent a transformation by a matrix in the way we have described, the image of the origin O is O; thus we can only use this method of representing a transformation if the origin is a point which does not move.

- Rotations can only be represented in this way if the centre of rotation is at O.

- Reflections can only be represented in this way if the mirror line passes through O.

- Enlargements can only be represented in this way if the centre of enlargement is at O.

- Shears can only be represented in this way if each point moves parallel to a line l through O, and the distance each point moves is proportional to its distance from l.

This may seem to be a considerable restriction – but in practice it is still a very useful procedure!

Activity

Explain why it is not possible to represent translations by matrices in the way we have described.

Activity

A shear moves points parallel to the line l with equation $y = x$; the distance from a point to its image is proportional to the distance of the

Activity continued

point from ℓ; the point Q(2, 0) is mapped to Q'(4, 2), as shown in the diagram.

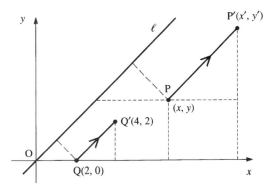

The point P has co-ordinates (x, y). By finding the co-ordinates of P', the image of P, in terms of x and y, show that this shear can be represented by a matrix, and find the matrix.

The columns of the matrix

Notice the effect of the transformation represented by the matrix

$\mathbf{M} = \begin{pmatrix} a & c \\ b & d \end{pmatrix}$ on the points I and J, with position vectors $\begin{pmatrix} 1 \\ 0 \end{pmatrix}$ and $\begin{pmatrix} 0 \\ 1 \end{pmatrix}$:

substituting $x = 1$, $y = 0$ in the defining equations $\begin{cases} x' = ax + cy \\ y' = bx + dy \end{cases}$ we

find that I', the image of I, has position vector $\begin{pmatrix} a \\ b \end{pmatrix}$, which is the first

column of matrix $\mathbf{M}$. Similarly J', the image of J, has position vector $\begin{pmatrix} c \\ d \end{pmatrix}$,

the second column of $\mathbf{M}$. This connection between the position vectors of I' and J' and the matrix representing a transformation provides us with a quick and usually easy way of finding the matrix. It does not, however, supply any information about whether or not the transformation can be represented by a matrix.

Activity

The diagrams on page 88 show the images of I and J following reflection in the line $y = x \tan\theta$ (i.e. the line through the origin forming an angle θ with the positive x axis). Find the co-ordinates of I' and J' and hence show

that the matrix which represents this reflection is $\begin{pmatrix} \cos 2\theta & \sin 2\theta \\ \sin 2\theta & -\cos 2\theta \end{pmatrix}$.

Activity continued

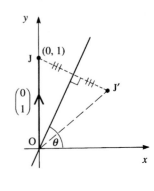

EXAMPLE

A transformation (known as a *projection*) maps each point on to the line ℓ in such a way that the line joining a point to its image is perpendicular to ℓ. If ℓ is the line $y = 2x$ show that the projection can be represented by a

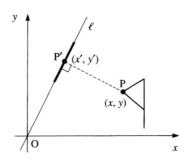

matrix, and that the matrix is $\begin{pmatrix} \frac{1}{5} & \frac{2}{5} \\ \frac{2}{5} & \frac{4}{5} \end{pmatrix}$.

Solution

$P'(x', y')$ is on $y = 2x \implies y' = 2x'$.

PP' is perpendicular to $y = 2x \implies$ gradient of $PP' = -\frac{1}{2}$ so that

$$\frac{y - y'}{x - x'} = -\frac{1}{2} \implies 2y - 2y' = -x + x'$$

Substituting for y' gives

$$2y - 4x' = -x + x'$$

so that

$$x' = \tfrac{1}{5}x + \tfrac{2}{5}y$$

and

$$y' = \tfrac{2}{5}x + \tfrac{4}{5}y$$

showing that the projection can be represented by the matrix $\begin{pmatrix} \frac{1}{5} & \frac{2}{5} \\ \frac{2}{5} & \frac{4}{5} \end{pmatrix}$.

The table opposite illustrates the common transformations of the plane and their matrices.

Transformation		Matrix	Transformation		Matrix
Reflection in x axis		$\begin{pmatrix} 1 & 0 \\ 0 & -1 \end{pmatrix}$	Reflection in y axis		$\begin{pmatrix} -1 & 0 \\ 0 & 1 \end{pmatrix}$
Reflection in $y = -x$		$\begin{pmatrix} 0 & -1 \\ -1 & 0 \end{pmatrix}$	Reflection in $y = x \tan\theta$		$\begin{pmatrix} \cos 2\theta & \sin 2\theta \\ \sin 2\theta & -\cos 2\theta \end{pmatrix}$
Rotation 90° anticlockwise about O		$\begin{pmatrix} 0 & -1 \\ 1 & 0 \end{pmatrix}$	Rotation 90° clockwise about O		$\begin{pmatrix} 0 & 1 \\ -1 & 0 \end{pmatrix}$
Half-turn about origin		$\begin{pmatrix} -1 & 0 \\ 0 & -1 \end{pmatrix}$	Rotation θ anticlockwise about origin		$\begin{pmatrix} \cos\theta & -\sin\theta \\ \sin\theta & \cos\theta \end{pmatrix}$
Enlargement $\times k$, centre O		$\begin{pmatrix} k & 0 \\ 0 & k \end{pmatrix}$	Two-way stretch $\times a$ horizontally $\times b$ vertically		$\begin{pmatrix} a & 0 \\ 0 & b \end{pmatrix}$
Shear parallel to x axis, $\times k$		$\begin{pmatrix} 1 & k \\ 0 & 1 \end{pmatrix}$	Shear parallel to y axis, $\times k$		$\begin{pmatrix} 1 & 0 \\ k & 1 \end{pmatrix}$
Projection on to x axis		$\begin{pmatrix} 1 & 0 \\ 0 & 0 \end{pmatrix}$	Projection on to y axis		$\begin{pmatrix} 0 & 0 \\ 0 & 1 \end{pmatrix}$

Transformations in three dimensions

So far our work has been applied to sets of points in a plane (i.e. two dimensions), using the plane as both the domain and co-domain of our transformations. Similar procedures work when we use three-dimensional space as the domain and co-domain.

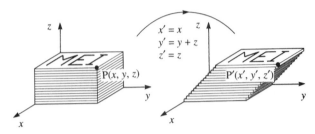

Figure 4.3

The shear illustrated in figure 4.3 is defined by the equations: $\begin{cases} x' = x \\ y' = y + z \\ z' = z \end{cases}$

so we represent this transformation by the matrix of coefficients $\begin{pmatrix} 1 & 0 & 0 \\ 0 & 1 & 1 \\ 0 & 0 & 1 \end{pmatrix}$.

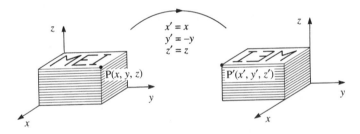

Figure 4.4

Reflection in the plane $y = 0$ (figure 4.4) is represented by the matrix $\begin{pmatrix} 1 & 0 & 0 \\ 0 & -1 & 0 \\ 0 & 0 & 1 \end{pmatrix}$.

It is not necessary for the domain and co-domain of a transformation to be the same. For example, when we draw the plan of a building to a scale of $1 : 100$, we start with an object in three-dimensional space and finish with a plane drawing. This might be as illustrated in figure 4.5, in which case the transformation would be represented by the matrix $\begin{pmatrix} \frac{1}{100} & 0 & 0 \\ 0 & \frac{1}{100} & 0 \end{pmatrix}$.

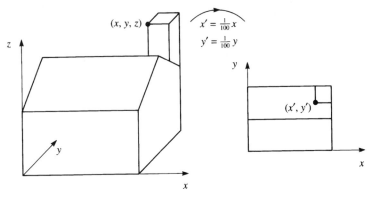

Figure 4.5

A similar transformation is the basis of the geographer's orthographic projection, often used for mapping the polar regions of the world.

Notice how the shape of the matrix depends on the dimensions of the domain and co-domain: a matrix with m rows and n columns is used to specify a transformation from n-dimensional space to m-dimensional space, where (for the moment) m and n are restricted to the values 1, 2 and 3.

For Discussion

What is meant by one-dimensional space? Is it part of two-dimensional space? Is two-dimensional space part of three-dimensional space?

Exercise 4A

1. Draw separate diagrams to show the effect of the following transformations on the object shown below, based on the unit square.

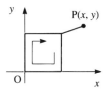

In each case find the co-ordinates of P′, the image P, in terms of x and y, and hence find the matrix of the transformation.

(i) Enlargement, centre the origin, scale factor 3.

(ii) Reflection in the x axis.

(iii) Reflection in the line $x + y = 0$.

(iv) Rotation 90° clockwise about O.

(v) Enlargement, scale factor $\frac{1}{2}$, centre O.

2. Draw diagrams to show the effect of the transformations represented by the following matrices, and so give full descriptions of the transformation.

(a) $\begin{pmatrix} 1 & 0 \\ 0 & -1 \end{pmatrix}$ (b) $\begin{pmatrix} 0 & 1 \\ 1 & 0 \end{pmatrix}$ (c) $\begin{pmatrix} 2 & 0 \\ 0 & 3 \end{pmatrix}$

(d) $\begin{pmatrix} 3 & 0 \\ 0 & 3 \end{pmatrix}$ (e) $\begin{pmatrix} \frac{1}{\sqrt{2}} & -\frac{1}{\sqrt{2}} \\ \frac{1}{\sqrt{2}} & \frac{1}{\sqrt{2}} \end{pmatrix}$ (f) $\begin{pmatrix} 0.6 & -0.8 \\ 0.8 & 0.6 \end{pmatrix}$

(g) $\begin{pmatrix} 2 & 0 \\ 0 & \frac{1}{2} \end{pmatrix}$ (h) $\begin{pmatrix} 2 & 1 \\ -1 & 0 \end{pmatrix}$ (i) $\begin{pmatrix} 1 & 0 \\ 0 & 0 \end{pmatrix}$

3. Triangle ABC has its vertices at $(2, 0)$, $(-1, 2)$ and $(1, 4)$. Triangle ABC is mapped to triangle A'B'C' by the transformation defined by the matrix $\begin{pmatrix} 4 & 3 \\ 5 & 4 \end{pmatrix}$. Find the co-ordinates of A', B', and C' and show that the area of the triangle has not been changed by the transformation.

4. A transformation maps P to P' as follows:

   ● each point is mapped on to the line $y = x$;

   ● the line joining a point to its image is parallel to the y axis.

   Find the co-ordinates of the image of the point (x, y) and hence show that this transformation can be represented by means of a matrix. What is that matrix?

5. Plot the points $(1, 0)$, $(1, 2)$, $(2, 2)$, $(2, 1)$, $(1, 1)$ and join them up to form a square flag on a vertical pole. Transform the flag by means of the matrix $\begin{pmatrix} 0 & -1 \\ 1 & 2 \end{pmatrix}$, and show the image on your diagram. Describe the transformation as simply as you can and show that the area of the flag has remained constant.

6. A transformation is represented by the matrix $\begin{pmatrix} 3 & -4 \\ 1 & -1 \end{pmatrix}$.

   (i) Choosing several points of your own, find the co-ordinates of the image points.

   (ii) Write down the vectors joining each point to its image. What do you notice?

   (iii) Describe this transformation.

7. Find the matrices which represent the following transformations of three-dimensional space:

   (a) enlargement, centre O, scale factor 3;

Exercise 4A continued

    (b) rotation 180° about the z axis;

    (c) reflection in the plane $y = z$.

8. Describe the transformations represented by these matrices

(a) $\begin{pmatrix} 1 & 0 & 0 \\ 0 & -1 & 0 \\ 0 & 0 & -1 \end{pmatrix}$ (b) $\begin{pmatrix} 0 & 1 & 0 \\ 1 & 0 & 0 \\ 0 & 0 & 1 \end{pmatrix}$ (c) $\begin{pmatrix} 1 & 0 & 3 \\ 0 & 1 & 0 \\ 0 & 0 & 1 \end{pmatrix}$ (d) $\begin{pmatrix} 0 & 0.01 & 0 \\ 0 & 0 & 0.01 \end{pmatrix}$

Properties of matrices

In the previous section we used the word 'matrix' for an array of numbers, such as $\begin{pmatrix} 3 & 0 \\ 0 & 1 \end{pmatrix}$, giving information about how to find the position of an image point following a transformation. Although this chapter is mainly concerned with transformation matrices, matrices have many other uses, some of which are explored briefly in Exercise 4B.

Any rectangular array of numbers is known as a matrix. It is usual to represent matrices by capital letters, often in bold print. (In handwriting we often use a capital letter with a line or squiggle under it.)

The order of a matrix

A matrix consists of rows and columns, and the entries in the various cells are known as *elements*. The matrix $\mathbf{M} = \begin{pmatrix} 5 & 1 & 0 \\ 4 & -1 & 3 \end{pmatrix}$ has 6 elements, arranged in 2 rows and 3 columns. We describe $\mathbf{M}$ as a 2 × 3 matrix, and this is known as the *order* of the matrix. It is important to note that we state the number of rows first, then the number of columns. The column vector $\begin{pmatrix} 1 \\ 0 \end{pmatrix}$ is an example of a 2 × 1 matrix; the column vector $\begin{pmatrix} 2 \\ -3 \\ 5 \end{pmatrix}$ is a 3 × 1 matrix. (Column vectors are sometimes called column matrices; they are often represented by lower case bold letters, such as $\mathbf{p}$ or $\mathbf{v}$.)

Matrices such as $\begin{pmatrix} 1 & 3 & -2 \\ -7 & 5 & 4 \\ 9 & 0 & 6 \end{pmatrix}$ and $\begin{pmatrix} 3 & 2 \\ 5 & 3 \end{pmatrix}$ which have the same number of rows as columns are known as *square matrices*.

Equality of matrices

Two matrices are equal if and only if they have the same order, and each element in one matrix is equal to the corresponding element in the other matrix. If, for example,

$$\mathbf{A} = \begin{pmatrix} 1 & 3 \\ 2 & 4 \end{pmatrix} \quad \mathbf{B} = \begin{pmatrix} 1 & 2 \\ 3 & 4 \end{pmatrix} \quad \mathbf{C} = \begin{pmatrix} 1 & 3 & 0 \\ 2 & 4 & 0 \end{pmatrix} \quad \mathbf{D} = \begin{pmatrix} 1 & 3 \\ 2 & 4 \end{pmatrix}$$

the three matrices $\mathbf{A}$, $\mathbf{B}$, $\mathbf{C}$ are not equal to each other, but $\mathbf{A}$ and $\mathbf{D}$ are.

Addition and subtraction of matrices

Matrices of the *same order* may be added or subtracted element by element:

$$\begin{pmatrix} 1 & 3 \\ 2 & 4 \end{pmatrix} + \begin{pmatrix} 5 & 0 \\ -2 & 7 \end{pmatrix} = \begin{pmatrix} 6 & 3 \\ 0 & 11 \end{pmatrix}$$

$$\begin{pmatrix} 1 & 4 \\ 2 & 5 \\ 3 & 6 \end{pmatrix} - \begin{pmatrix} 4 & -2 \\ -3 & 7 \\ 5 & 6 \end{pmatrix} = \begin{pmatrix} -3 & 6 \\ 5 & -2 \\ -2 & 0 \end{pmatrix}$$

But we cannot evaluate $\begin{pmatrix} 1 & 3 \\ 2 & 4 \end{pmatrix} + \begin{pmatrix} 1 \\ 0 \end{pmatrix}$ because the matrices are not of the same order. We say they are incompatible, or do not conform.

The matrix $\mathbf{O} = \begin{pmatrix} 0 & 0 \\ 0 & 0 \end{pmatrix}$ is known as the 2×2 *zero matrix*.

Activity

Explain why matrix addition is

(i) commutative, i.e. $\mathbf{A} + \mathbf{B} = \mathbf{B} + \mathbf{A}$;

(ii) associative, i.e. $\mathbf{A} + (\mathbf{B} + \mathbf{C}) = (\mathbf{A} + \mathbf{B}) + \mathbf{C}$.

Multiplying a matrix by a number

We multiply a matrix by a number by multiplying each element by that number:

$$3 \times \begin{pmatrix} 1 & 3 \\ 2 & 4 \end{pmatrix} = \begin{pmatrix} 3 & 9 \\ 6 & 12 \end{pmatrix}$$

Multiplication of matrices

At first sight matrix multiplication looks complicated and artificial. But with practice you will find it straightforward. There are good reasons for our strange routines as you will see on page 106!

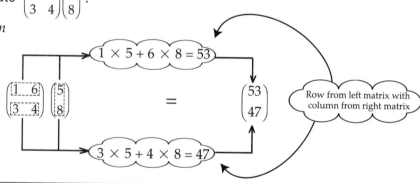

The transformation defined by the matrix $\mathbf{M} = \begin{pmatrix} 2 & 5 \\ 4 & 3 \end{pmatrix}$ maps the point P

with position vector $\mathbf{p} = \begin{pmatrix} x \\ y \end{pmatrix}$ to the point P′ with position vector

$\mathbf{p}' = \begin{pmatrix} x' \\ y' \end{pmatrix}$ where

$$\begin{cases} x' = 2x + 5y \\ y' = 4x + 3y \end{cases}$$

So we may write

$$\mathbf{p}' = \begin{pmatrix} 2x + 5y \\ 4x + 3y \end{pmatrix}$$

The 2×1 matrix $\mathbf{p}'$ above is an example of a matrix product; it is the product of the 2×2 matrix $\mathbf{M}$ with the 2×1 matrix $\mathbf{p}$, *in that order*:

$$\begin{pmatrix} 2 & 5 \\ 4 & 3 \end{pmatrix} \begin{pmatrix} x \\ y \end{pmatrix} = \begin{pmatrix} 2x + 5y \\ 4x + 3y \end{pmatrix}$$

EXAMPLE Calculate $\begin{pmatrix} 1 & 6 \\ 3 & 4 \end{pmatrix} \begin{pmatrix} 5 \\ 8 \end{pmatrix}$.

Solution

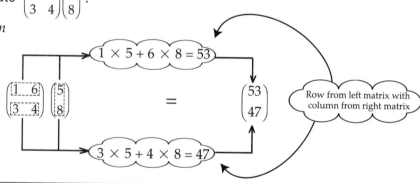

$$\begin{pmatrix} 1 & 6 \\ 3 & 4 \end{pmatrix} \begin{pmatrix} 5 \\ 8 \end{pmatrix} = \begin{pmatrix} 53 \\ 47 \end{pmatrix}$$

$1 \times 5 + 6 \times 8 = 53$

$3 \times 5 + 4 \times 8 = 47$

Row from left matrix with column from right matrix

Activity

The diagram shows flag ABCD and its image A′B′C′D′ after applying the rotation matrix $\begin{pmatrix} 0.8 & -0.6 \\ 0.6 & 0.8 \end{pmatrix}$.

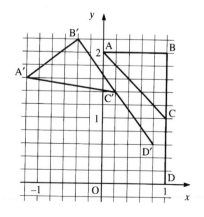

Activity continued on page 96

Activity continued

By calculating $\begin{pmatrix} 0.8 & -0.6 \\ 0.6 & 0.8 \end{pmatrix}\begin{pmatrix} 0 \\ 2 \end{pmatrix}$, $\begin{pmatrix} 0.8 & -0.6 \\ 0.6 & 0.8 \end{pmatrix}\begin{pmatrix} 1 \\ 2 \end{pmatrix}$ and two other matrix

products, check that A′, B′, C′ and D′ have been plotted correctly.

A similar technique applies to all matrix multiplications. You use each row of the first (i.e. left) matrix with each column, in turn, of the second matrix. We show in figure 4.6 the steps used when multiplying a 2 × 2 matrix by a 2 × 3 matrix. The product is another 2 × 3 matrix.

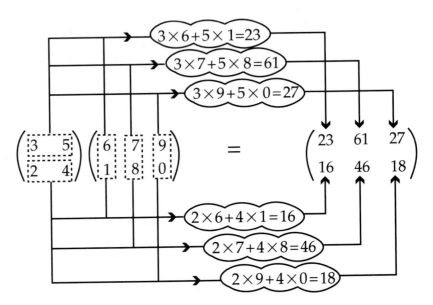

Figure 4.6

The four matrix multiplications of the last activity can be combined into one matrix multiplication:

$$\begin{pmatrix} 0.8 & -0.6 \\ 0.6 & 0.8 \end{pmatrix}\begin{pmatrix} 0 & 1 & 1 & 1 \\ 2 & 2 & 1 & 0 \end{pmatrix} = \begin{pmatrix} -1.2 & -0.4 & 0.2 & 0.8 \\ 1.6 & 2.2 & 1.4 & 0.6 \end{pmatrix}$$

If you multiply a 3 × 4 matrix (on the left) by a 4 × 2 matrix (on the right) similar rules apply; the product is a 3 × 2 matrix. For example:

$$\begin{pmatrix} 1 & 2 & 4 & 7 \\ -3 & 5 & 0 & 1 \\ 4 & 2 & 3 & 5 \end{pmatrix}\begin{pmatrix} 5 & 1 \\ -6 & 4 \\ 8 & 9 \\ 2 & 2 \end{pmatrix} = \begin{pmatrix} 39 & 59 \\ -43 & 19 \\ 42 & 49 \end{pmatrix}$$

Properties of matrix multiplication

Matrices must be conformable for multiplication

To be able to multiply two matrices together the number of columns in the first (left) matrix must equal the number of rows in the second matrix. If the first matrix is 3×4, the second must be $4 \times$ something. We say that the matrices need to *conform*. Generally, if $\mathbf{M}$ is $p \times q$, and $\mathbf{N}$ is $q \times r$, the product $\mathbf{MN}$ exists and is of order $p \times r$. It may be helpful to think of the rules for joining dominoes end to end.

$$\boxed{p \times q}\;\boxed{q \times r} \quad \text{gives} \quad \boxed{p \times r}$$

Matrix multiplication is not commutative

If $\mathbf{A} = \begin{pmatrix} 3 & 1 \\ 2 & 7 \end{pmatrix}$ and $\mathbf{B} = \begin{pmatrix} 4 & -2 \\ 1 & 5 \end{pmatrix}$ the product $\mathbf{AB}$ is given by

$$\mathbf{AB} = \begin{pmatrix} 3 & 1 \\ 2 & 7 \end{pmatrix}\begin{pmatrix} 4 & -2 \\ 1 & 5 \end{pmatrix} = \begin{pmatrix} 13 & -1 \\ 15 & 31 \end{pmatrix}$$

and the product $\mathbf{BA}$ by

$$\mathbf{BA} = \begin{pmatrix} 4 & -2 \\ 1 & 5 \end{pmatrix}\begin{pmatrix} 3 & 1 \\ 2 & 7 \end{pmatrix} = \begin{pmatrix} 8 & -10 \\ 13 & 36 \end{pmatrix}$$

As $\mathbf{AB} \neq \mathbf{BA}$, matrix multiplication is not commutative. It matters which way round you write your matrices. Indeed, sometimes the product $\mathbf{MN}$ exists but the product $\mathbf{NM}$ does not exist, because the number of columns in $\mathbf{N}$ does not match the number of rows in $\mathbf{M}$. For example if

$$\mathbf{M} = \begin{pmatrix} 2 & -4 \\ 5 & 3 \end{pmatrix} \quad \text{and} \quad \mathbf{N} = \begin{pmatrix} 6 & -2 & 7 \\ 4 & 3 & -5 \end{pmatrix}$$

then

$$\mathbf{MN} = \begin{pmatrix} 2 & -4 \\ 5 & 3 \end{pmatrix}\begin{pmatrix} 6 & -2 & 7 \\ 4 & 3 & -5 \end{pmatrix} = \begin{pmatrix} -4 & -16 & 34 \\ 42 & -1 & 20 \end{pmatrix};$$

but the product $\mathbf{NM} = \begin{pmatrix} 6 & -2 & 7 \\ 4 & 3 & -5 \end{pmatrix}\begin{pmatrix} 2 & -4 \\ 5 & 3 \end{pmatrix}$ is not defined.

Matrix multiplication is associative

Whenever matrices $\mathbf{P}, \mathbf{Q}, \mathbf{R}$ are conformable for multiplication, $(\mathbf{PQ})\mathbf{R} = \mathbf{P}(\mathbf{QR})$. This is the associative property of matrix multiplication. We prove it on page 106.

Activity

Using $\mathbf{P} = \begin{pmatrix} 2 & 4 \\ -3 & 1 \end{pmatrix}$, $\mathbf{Q} = \begin{pmatrix} 5 & -3 \\ 1 & 2 \end{pmatrix}$ and $\mathbf{R} = \begin{pmatrix} 4 & -3 \\ 2 & 1 \end{pmatrix}$ calculate

(i) $\mathbf{PQ}$, (ii) $(\mathbf{PQ})\mathbf{R}$, (iii) $\mathbf{QR}$, (iv) $\mathbf{P}(\mathbf{QR})$, and so demonstrate the associative property of matrix multiplication.

Matrix multiplication is distributive over matrix addition

Provided the matrices **P, Q, R** conform so that the sums and products exist,

$$P(Q + R) = PQ + PR$$

It may also be proved that

$$(P + Q)R = PR + QR$$

These two properties are what we mean when we say that matrix multiplication is distributive over matrix addition.

For Discussion

(a) Choose any three 2×2 matrices **P, Q, R** and check by direct evaluation that $P(Q + R) = PQ + PR$.

(b) By considering the elements in corresponding columns of the three matrices **B, C** and **B + C**, show that $A(B + C) = AB + AC$.

The identity matrix

Whenever you multiply a 2×2 matrix **M** by $I = \begin{pmatrix} 1 & 0 \\ 0 & 1 \end{pmatrix}$ the product is **M**.

It makes no difference whether you pre-multiply by **I**, as in

$$\begin{pmatrix} 1 & 0 \\ 0 & 1 \end{pmatrix}\begin{pmatrix} 3 & 5 \\ 7 & -2 \end{pmatrix} = \begin{pmatrix} 3 & 5 \\ 7 & -2 \end{pmatrix}$$

or post-multiply by **I**, as in

$$\begin{pmatrix} a & c \\ b & d \end{pmatrix}\begin{pmatrix} 1 & 0 \\ 0 & 1 \end{pmatrix} = \begin{pmatrix} a & c \\ b & d \end{pmatrix}$$

For multiplication of 2×2 matrices, **I** behaves in the same way as the number 1 when dealing with multiplication of real numbers. **I** is known as the 2×2 *identity matrix*.

The 3×3 identity matrix (which we shall denote by I_3) is $\begin{pmatrix} 1 & 0 & 0 \\ 0 & 1 & 0 \\ 0 & 0 & 1 \end{pmatrix}$.

Activity

Show that $I_3M = M$ and $MI_3 = M$ for any 3×3 matrix you like to choose.

For Discussion

Why is there no such thing as a 2×3 identity matrix?

Inverse matrices

Let $\mathbf{A} = \begin{pmatrix} 4 & 2 \\ 5 & 3 \end{pmatrix}$ and $\mathbf{B} = \begin{pmatrix} 3 & -2 \\ -5 & 4 \end{pmatrix}$. Then $\mathbf{AB} = \begin{pmatrix} 4 & 2 \\ 5 & 3 \end{pmatrix}\begin{pmatrix} 3 & -2 \\ -5 & 4 \end{pmatrix} = \begin{pmatrix} 2 & 0 \\ 0 & 2 \end{pmatrix}$.

Therefore the product of $\mathbf{A}$ and $\frac{1}{2}\mathbf{B}$ is $\begin{pmatrix} 1 & 0 \\ 0 & 1 \end{pmatrix}$.

If the product of two square matrices, $\mathbf{M}$ and $\mathbf{N}$, is the identity matrix, $\mathbf{N}$ is known as the *inverse* of $\mathbf{M}$. We write $\mathbf{N} = \mathbf{M}^{-1}$.

Activity

Suppose $\mathbf{M}^{-1} = \begin{pmatrix} w & y \\ x & z \end{pmatrix}$ where $\mathbf{M} = \begin{pmatrix} a & c \\ b & d \end{pmatrix}$. Multiply these two matrices together, equate the result to $\begin{pmatrix} 1 & 0 \\ 0 & 1 \end{pmatrix}$ and so form two pairs of equations. Solve these as pairs of simultaneous equations, to show that

$$\mathbf{M}^{-1} = \frac{1}{\Delta}\begin{pmatrix} d & -c \\ -b & a \end{pmatrix},\text{ where } \Delta = ad - bc, \text{ provided } \Delta \neq 0.$$

The number $ad - bc$ is known as the *determinant* of the 2×2 matrix. If the determinant is 0, the matrix $\begin{pmatrix} a & c \\ b & d \end{pmatrix}$ does not have an inverse, and is described as *singular*.

EXAMPLE

Find the inverses of the matrices (a) $\begin{pmatrix} 7 & 8 \\ 3 & 4 \end{pmatrix}$ and (b) $\begin{pmatrix} 2 & 8 \\ 1 & 4 \end{pmatrix}$.

Solution

(a) $\begin{pmatrix} 7 & 8 \\ 3 & 4 \end{pmatrix} = \frac{1}{4}\begin{pmatrix} 4 & -8 \\ -3 & 7 \end{pmatrix}$ which may be written as $\begin{pmatrix} 1 & -2 \\ -\frac{3}{4} & \frac{7}{4} \end{pmatrix}$.

$7 \times 4 - 3 \times 8 = 4$

Interchange the elements on the leading diagonal (from top left to bottom right) and change the sign of the two other elements

(b) The determinant of $\begin{pmatrix} 2 & 8 \\ 1 & 4 \end{pmatrix}$ is $2 \times 4 - 1 \times 8 = 0$ so $\begin{pmatrix} 2 & 8 \\ 1 & 4 \end{pmatrix}$ has no inverse.

As matrix multiplication is not commutative, you may have been wondering if it matters in which order you multiply the two matrices in the last activity. In the following example we prove that it does not matter whether we pre-multiply $\mathbf{M}$ by $\mathbf{M}^{-1}$ (forming $\mathbf{M}^{-1}\mathbf{M}$) or post-multiply $\mathbf{M}$ by $\mathbf{M}^{-1}$ (forming $\mathbf{MM}^{-1}$) the product is $\mathbf{I}$, the identity matrix.

EXAMPLE

M is a square matrix, and L and R are matrices such that $\mathbf{LM} = \mathbf{I}$ and $\mathbf{MR} = \mathbf{I}$. Prove that $\mathbf{L} = \mathbf{R}$.

Solution

$$\mathbf{LM} = \mathbf{I}$$

$$\Rightarrow (\mathbf{LM})\mathbf{R} = \mathbf{IR}$$

$$\Rightarrow \mathbf{L}(\mathbf{MR}) = \mathbf{R}$$

$$\Rightarrow \mathbf{LI} = \mathbf{R}$$

$$\Rightarrow \mathbf{L} = \mathbf{R}$$

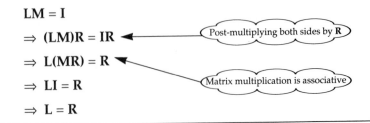

Post-multiplying both sides by **R**

Matrix multiplication is associative

This is an important result: it means that the inverse of a matrix (if it exists) is unique. It applies to all (square) matrices, not just 2×2 matrices.

If the determinant of a square matrix is not 0 the inverse of the matrix exists, and the matrix is described as *non-singular*. The determinant of a *singular* matrix is 0.

At the end of Chapter 5 we show you how to find the determinant of a 3×3 matrix, but further work on the inverses of 3×3 matrices is left to Pure Mathematics 6.

Activity

If your calculator handles matrices find out how you should input them. Particularly notice whether the calculator encourages you to input by rows or by columns. Find out how to add and multiply matrices on your calculator, and how to find the inverse of a matrix.

HISTORICAL NOTE

The multiplication of matrices was first fully defined by Arthur Cayley (1821–1895) in 1858. Cayley's mathematical talent was noticed while at school (in London), and his first mathematical paper was published in 1841, while he was an undergraduate at Cambridge. He worked as a lawyer for some 14 years, refusing more cases than he accepted as he only wanted to earn sufficient to enable him to get on with 'his work'; during this period he published nearly 200 mathematical papers. In 1863 he returned to Cambridge as a professor. As well as his work on matrices, he developed the geometry of n-dimensional spaces and is known for his work on the theory of invariants, much of this in conjunction with his life-long friend, James Joseph Sylvester (1814–1897). It was Sylvester who, in 1850, coined the word 'matrix', Latin for 'womb'; in geology a matrix is a mass of rock enclosing gems; so in mathematics a matrix is a container of (valuable) information. It was at about this time that Florence Nightingale was one of Sylvester's pupils.

Exercise 4B

In Questions 1 – 4 use:

$$A = \begin{pmatrix} 3 & 1 \\ 2 & 4 \end{pmatrix} \qquad B = \begin{pmatrix} -3 & 7 \\ 2 & 5 \end{pmatrix} \qquad C = \begin{pmatrix} 2 & 3 & 4 \\ 5 & 7 & 1 \end{pmatrix}$$

$$D = \begin{pmatrix} 3 & 4 \\ 7 & 0 \\ 1 & -2 \end{pmatrix} \qquad E = \begin{pmatrix} 4 & 7 \\ 3 & -2 \\ 1 & 5 \end{pmatrix} \qquad F = \begin{pmatrix} 3 & 7 & -5 \\ 2 & 6 & 0 \\ -1 & 4 & 8 \end{pmatrix}$$

1. Calculate (if possible)

(a) **A + B**   (b) **3C**   (c) **B + C**   (d) **C − D**   (e) **D − E**

(f) **AB**   (g) **CA**   (h) **BC**   (i) **CD**   (j) **DC**

(k) **AF**   (l) **BE**   (m) **4F + EC**   (n) **EA**   (o) **FE**

2. By calculating (if possible) **AB, BA, AD** and **DA** demonstrate that matrix multiplication is not commutative.

3. Demonstrate the associative property of matrix multiplication by calculating both **(AC)F** and **A(CF)**.

4. Calculate (a) A^{-1}; (b) B^{-1}; (c) **AB**; (d) $(AB)^{-1}$.
Is $(AB)^{-1}$ the same as $A^{-1}B^{-1}$ or the same as $B^{-1}A^{-1}$?

5. Where possible find the inverses of the following matrices:

(a) $\begin{pmatrix} 4 & 3 \\ 6 & 5 \end{pmatrix}$ (b) $\begin{pmatrix} 6 & -3 \\ -4 & -2 \end{pmatrix}$ (c) $\begin{pmatrix} 5 & 6 \\ 2 & 3 \end{pmatrix}$ (d) $\begin{pmatrix} \frac{1}{3} & \frac{3}{4} \\ \frac{2}{3} & 2 \end{pmatrix}$ (e) $\begin{pmatrix} e & f \\ g & h \end{pmatrix}$

6. The matrix $\begin{pmatrix} 1-k & 2 \\ -1 & 4-k \end{pmatrix}$ is singular. Find the possible values of k.

7. The diagram shows a flag.

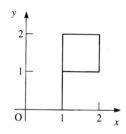

(i) Use the matrix $\begin{pmatrix} -0.6 & 0.8 \\ 0.8 & 0.6 \end{pmatrix}$ to transform the flag, and draw the original flag and its image on one diagram.

(ii) Describe the transformation in words.

4

Exercise 4B continued

8. Triangle T has its vertices at $(1, 0)$, $(0, 1)$ and $(-2, 0)$. It is transformed to triangle T′ by means of the matrix $\mathbf{M} = \begin{pmatrix} 3 & 1 \\ 1 & 1 \end{pmatrix}$.

   (i) Find the co-ordinates of the vertices of T′, and show T and T′ on one diagram.

   (ii) Find the ratio of the area of T′ to the area of T, and the value of the determinant of $\mathbf{M}$.

9. (i) Choose a shape of your own. Call it S.

   (ii) Transform S using the matrix $\mathbf{M} = \begin{pmatrix} 2 & 1 \\ 1 & -2 \end{pmatrix}$ to form the image S′. Draw S′.

   (iii) Calculate $\mathbf{M}^2$.

   (iv) Describe as simply as you can the single transformation represented by $\mathbf{M}^2$.

10. $\mathbf{A} = \begin{pmatrix} 5 & 3 \\ 6 & 4 \end{pmatrix}$ $\mathbf{B} = \begin{pmatrix} 4 & 3 \\ 1 & 2 \end{pmatrix}$. Calculate

    (i) $\mathbf{A}^{-1}$ (ii) $\mathbf{B}^{-1}$ (iii) $\mathbf{A}^{-1}\mathbf{B}^{-1}$ (iv) $\mathbf{B}^{-1}\mathbf{A}^{-1}$

    (v) $(\mathbf{BA})^{-1}$ (vi) $(\mathbf{AB})^{-1}$

    Comment on your results.

11. The matrix $\mathbf{S} = \begin{pmatrix} 5 & 0 & 1 & 6 & 2 \\ 7 & 8 & 4 & 3 & 9 \end{pmatrix}$ contains the numbers of first and second class stamps used in my office each day last week. (Top row denotes first class.)

    (i) Find a matrix $\mathbf{D}$ such that $\mathbf{DS}$ gives the total number of stamps used each day.

    (ii) Find a matrix $\mathbf{N}$ such that $\mathbf{SN}$ gives the total number of each type of stamp used in the week.

    (iii) First class stamps cost 25 pence while second class stamps cost 19 pence. Find a way of calculating the total cost of last week's stamps using only matrix multiplication.

12. The stylised map on page 103 shows the bus routes in a holiday area. Lines represent routes that run each way between the resorts. Arrows indicate one-way scenic routes. $\mathbf{M}$ is the partly completed 4×4 matrix which shows the number of direct routes between the various resorts. Copy and complete $\mathbf{M}$. Calculate $\mathbf{M}^2$ and explain what information it contains. What information would $\mathbf{M}^3$ contain?

Exercise 4B continued

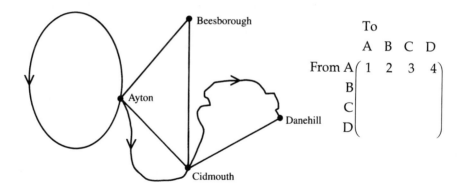

	To			
	A	B	C	D
From A	1	2	3	4
B				
C				
D				

13. The figure shows the start of the plaiting process, using three strands, a, b and c.

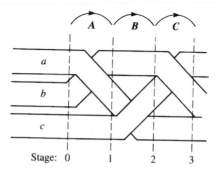

The process has only two steps, repeated alternately:

A: cross the top strand *over* the middle strand;

B: cross the middle strand *under* the bottom strand.

At Stage 0 the order of the strands is given by $s_0 = \begin{pmatrix} a \\ b \\ c \end{pmatrix}$.

(i) Show that pre-multiplying s_0 by the matrix $A = \begin{pmatrix} 0 & 1 & 0 \\ 1 & 0 & 0 \\ 0 & 0 & 1 \end{pmatrix}$ gives s_1, the vector which represents the order of the strands at Stage 1.

(ii) Find the 3×3 matrix B which represents the transition from Stage 1 to Stage 2.

(ii) Find matrix $M = BA$ and show that Ms_0 gives s_2, the vector which represents the order of the strands at Stage 2.

(iv) Find M^2 and hence find the order of the strands at Stage 4.

(v) Calculate M^3. What does this tell you?

14. There are two basic types of four-terminal electrical network (see diagram).

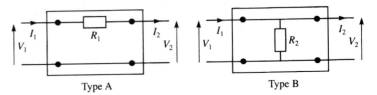

Type A   Type B

(i) In Type A the output voltage V_2 and current I_2 are related to the input voltage V_1 and current I_1 by the simultaneous equations

$$V_2 = V_1 - I_1 R_1$$
$$I_2 = I_1$$

We may write $\begin{pmatrix} V_2 \\ I_2 \end{pmatrix} = \mathbf{A} \begin{pmatrix} V_1 \\ I_1 \end{pmatrix}$. Write down matrix **A**.

(ii) In Type B the corresponding simultaneous equations are

$$V_2 = V_1$$
$$I_2 = I_1 - \frac{V_1}{R_2}$$

Write down the matrix **B** which represents the effect of a Type B network.

(iii) Find the matrix which represents the effect of Type A followed by Type B.

(iv) Is the effect of Type B followed by Type A the same as the effect of Type A followed by Type B?

Properties of transformations

Notation

We often use a single letter such as T to represent a transformation. Then the image of the point P may be denoted by $T(P)$ or by P′. The point P has position vector **p**; its image $T(P)$ has position vector **p′** = $T(\mathbf{p})$. We find $T(\mathbf{p})$ by evaluating the matrix product **Tp**, where **T** is the matrix which represents T.

Composition of transformations

If we use X to represent reflection in the x axis, then X maps the point P to the point $X(P)$, figure 4.7.

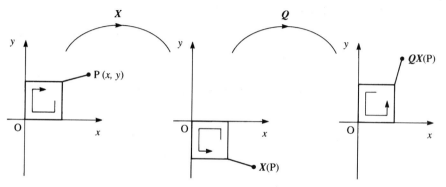

Figure 4.7

If Q represents a quarter turn anticlockwise about O, and we apply Q to the image formed by X, the point $X(P)$ is mapped to $Q(X(P))$ which we shall abbreviate to $QX(P)$. The composite transformation

reflection in the x axis followed by a quarter turn anticlockwise about O

is represented by QX. Note the order. From the diagram you will recognise that QX is equivalent to reflection in the line $y = x$.

Reflection X is represented by the matrix $\mathbf{X} = \begin{pmatrix} 1 & 0 \\ 0 & -1 \end{pmatrix}$; the quarter turn

Q is represented by $\mathbf{Q} = \begin{pmatrix} 0 & -1 \\ 1 & 0 \end{pmatrix}$. Direct calculation will confirm that

the product $\mathbf{QX}$ is $\begin{pmatrix} 0 & 1 \\ 1 & 0 \end{pmatrix}$, the matrix which represents reflection in the line

$y = x$. Again notice the order in which the matrices were arranged for the multiplication: the matrix representing the first transformation is on the right, and the matrix for the second transformation is on the left. We now prove more generally that the matrix of this form of composite transformation is found by multiplying the matrices of the component transformations, in the correct order.

Transformations T and S are represented by the matrices $\mathbf{T} = \begin{pmatrix} a & c \\ b & d \end{pmatrix}$ and

$\mathbf{S} = \begin{pmatrix} p & r \\ q & s \end{pmatrix}$ respectively. Applying T to the point P with position

vector $\begin{pmatrix} x \\ y \end{pmatrix}$ we obtain P′ with position vector $\begin{pmatrix} x' \\ y' \end{pmatrix} = \begin{pmatrix} ax + cy \\ bx + dy \end{pmatrix}$. Then

applying S to P′ gives P″, with position vector $\begin{pmatrix} x'' \\ y'' \end{pmatrix}$, as shown in figure 4.8.

We use U to represent the composite transformation ST, T followed by S.

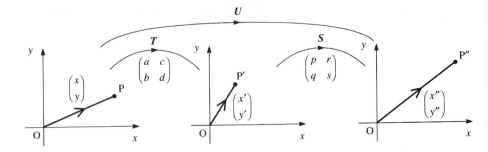

Figure 4.8

Then
$$x'' = px' + ry'$$
$$= p(ax + cy) + r(bx + dy) \quad \text{since } x' = ax + cy \text{ and } y' = bx + dy$$
$$= (pa + rb)x + (pc + rd)y$$

Similarly $y'' = (qa + sb)x + (qc + sd)y$

Thus the matrix for the composite transformation $U = ST$ is

$$\begin{pmatrix} pa + rb & pc + rd \\ qa + sb & qc + sd \end{pmatrix}$$

which is what we have already defined as the matrix product $\begin{pmatrix} p & r \\ q & s \end{pmatrix}\begin{pmatrix} a & c \\ b & d \end{pmatrix}$.

Proof that matrix multiplication is associative

We can extend this to combine three or more transformations. If L, M and N are three transformations, then $L(MN)$ represents the composite transformation

Do N first, then do M to the resulting figure, and finally do L to the image made by M.

If the corresponding matrices are **L**, **M** and **N** then the matrix representing $L(MN)$ is the product **L(MN)**. In essence, the matrix **L(MN)** represents the instructions

Apply N and then M, pause, and then apply L.

Similarly the matrix **(LM)N** represents the instructions

Apply N, pause, and then apply M and then L.

Where you pause makes no difference!

As both matrix products **L(MN)** and **(LM)N** represent the same sequence of transformations, applied in the same order, producing the same result, they represent the same composite transformation. We conclude that matrix multiplication is associative. It does not matter whether you calculate **L(MN)** or **(LM)N**; the brackets are superfluous, and are usually omitted.

For Discussion

What difference (if any) does it make to the above reasoning if

(i)   the order of matrices **L**, **M** and **N** is 3×3;

(ii) the matrices **L**, **M** and **N** are not square;

(iii) the order of the matrices is 4×4?

Inverses

We again use Q to represent a quarter turn anticlockwise about O; the corresponding matrix is $\mathbf{Q} = \begin{pmatrix} 0 & -1 \\ 1 & 0 \end{pmatrix}$. Check that det $\mathbf{Q} = 1$, and that

$\mathbf{Q}^{-1} = \begin{pmatrix} 0 & 1 \\ -1 & 0 \end{pmatrix}$. You will recognise $\mathbf{Q}^{-1}$ as the matrix which represents a quarter turn clockwise about O, the transformation which undoes the effect of Q. It is known as the inverse of Q, and is denoted by Q^{-1}. This is typical of the general pattern: if T is a transformation with matrix **T**, the *inverse* of T (if it exists) is the transformation denoted by T^{-1} which undoes the effect of T; T^{-1} has matrix $\mathbf{T}^{-1}$.

Now suppose we want to find the inverse of the product **AB**, where **A** and **B** are non-singular matrices, i.e. we want to find **X** such that $\mathbf{X(AB)} = \mathbf{I}$. Repeatedly using the fact that matrix multiplication is associative we have

$$\mathbf{X(AB)} = \mathbf{I}$$

$$\Rightarrow \quad \mathbf{(XA)B} = \mathbf{I} \qquad \text{(Matrix multiplication is associative)}$$

$$\Rightarrow \quad \mathbf{XA} = \mathbf{B}^{-1} \qquad \text{(Since the inverse of } \mathbf{B} \text{ is unique)}$$

$$\Rightarrow \quad \mathbf{(XA)A}^{-1} = \mathbf{B}^{-1}\mathbf{A}^{-1} \qquad \text{(Post-multiplying both sides by } \mathbf{A}^{-1}\text{)}$$

$$\Rightarrow \quad \mathbf{X(AA}^{-1}) = \mathbf{B}^{-1}\mathbf{A}^{-1} \qquad \text{(Matrix multiplication is associative)}$$

$$\Rightarrow \quad \mathbf{XI} = \mathbf{B}^{-1}\mathbf{A}^{-1}$$

$$\Rightarrow \quad \mathbf{X} = \mathbf{B}^{-1}\mathbf{A}^{-1}$$

Thus $\mathbf{(AB)}^{-1} = \mathbf{B}^{-1}\mathbf{A}^{-1}$, where **A** and **B** are non-singular matrices of the same order. You put your socks on before your shoes, but presumably you take your shoes off before your socks!

Activity

As often happens, it is easier when you know the answer! Use the associative property of matrix multiplication to show that $\mathbf{(AB)(B}^{-1}\mathbf{A}^{-1})$ simplifies to **I** and so provide an alternative proof that $\mathbf{(AB)}^{-1} = \mathbf{B}^{-1}\mathbf{A}^{-1}$.

Exercise 4C

1. X represents reflection in the x axis and J represents a quarter turn clockwise about the origin. Write down the matrices which represent X and J.

   (i) Find the matrix which represents JX. Describe the transformation JX as simply as you can.

   (ii) Repeat part (i) for the transformation XJ.

2. Transformations R and S are represented by matrices $\mathbf{R} = \begin{pmatrix} 2 & -1 \\ 1 & 3 \end{pmatrix}$

   and $\mathbf{S} = \begin{pmatrix} 3 & 0 \\ -2 & 4 \end{pmatrix}$. Find the matrix which represents the transformation RS.

3. Write down the matrix $\mathbf{M}$ which represents reflection of the plane in the line $y = x \tan \theta$. Show that $\mathbf{M}^{-1} = \mathbf{M}$, and verify that $\mathbf{M}^2 = \mathbf{I}$.

4. Write down the matrix $\mathbf{R}$ which represents rotation of the plane through angle α anticlockwise about the origin. Explain why it should be possible to obtain $\mathbf{R}^{-1}$ from $\mathbf{R}$ by replacing α by $-\alpha$. Verify that this is so.

5. Prove that $(\mathbf{PQ})^{-1} = \mathbf{Q}^{-1}\mathbf{P}^{-1}$ and verify the formula by direct calculation in the case $\mathbf{P} = \begin{pmatrix} 2 & 3 \\ 2 & 4 \end{pmatrix}$ and $\mathbf{Q} = \begin{pmatrix} 4 & 3 \\ 5 & 5 \end{pmatrix}$.

6. R_α and R_β represent rotation of the plane through angles α and β anticlockwise about the origin. The corresponding matrices are $\mathbf{R}_\alpha$ and $\mathbf{R}_\beta$.

   (i) By considering the effects of the rotations, explain why $\mathbf{R}_\alpha\mathbf{R}_\beta = \mathbf{R}_\beta\mathbf{R}_\alpha$.

   (ii) Write down $\mathbf{R}_\alpha$ and $\mathbf{R}_\beta$ and calculate $\mathbf{R}_\alpha\mathbf{R}_\beta$, simplifying your answer as much as possible.

   (iii) Describe as simply as possible a single transformation equivalent to $\mathbf{R}_\alpha\mathbf{R}_\beta$.

7. (i) Write down the matrix $\mathbf{R}$ which represents the rotation through $30°$ anticlockwise about the origin and the matrix $\mathbf{M}$ which represents reflection in the line $y = \sqrt{3}x$.

   (ii) Calculate $\mathbf{MR}$. What single transformation does this matrix represent?

   (iii) What single transformation does the matrix $\mathbf{RM}$ represent?

8. A shear S maps $(1, 0)$ to $(2, 3)$ and leaves the origin at the origin. Find the matrix $\mathbf{M}$ which represents S and verify that $\mathbf{M}^{-1}$ represents the shear that maps $(2, 3)$ to $(1, 0)$ and leaves the origin at the origin.

9. (a) Write down the matrix which represents rotation through angle 2α about O.

   (b) Write down the matrix which represents reflection in the line $y = x\tan\theta$.

   (c) Use matrix multiplication to show that a rotation followed by a reflection in a line which passes through the centre of the rotation is equivalent to a single reflection.

10. Two mirror lines intersect at O. The angle between the mirrors is θ. Use matrix multiplication to prove that reflection in one line followed by reflection in the other line is equivalent to a rotation of 2θ about O.

11. A matrix $\mathbf{M}$ defines an anticlockwise rotation about the origin through an angle θ, mapping the point (x, y) to (x', y'), where

$$\begin{pmatrix} x' \\ y' \end{pmatrix} = \mathbf{M}\begin{pmatrix} x \\ y \end{pmatrix}.$$

   (i) Show that $\mathbf{M} = \begin{pmatrix} \cos\theta & -\sin\theta \\ \sin\theta & \cos\theta \end{pmatrix}$.

   (ii) Write down the matrix which corresponds to an anticlockwise rotation of 135° about the origin.

   The lines $y = -4x$ and $y = 2x - 5\sqrt{2}$ are rotated anticlockwise through 135° about the origin.

   (iii) Show that the image of the line $y = -4x$ is $y = \frac{5}{3}x$.

   (iv) Find the equation of the image of the line $y = 2x - 5\sqrt{2}$.

   [MEI 1994]

12. (a) Two square matrices $\mathbf{M}$ and $\mathbf{N}$ (of the same size) have inverses $\mathbf{M}^{-1}$ and $\mathbf{N}^{-1}$ respectively. Show that the inverse of $\mathbf{MN}$ is $\mathbf{N}^{-1}\mathbf{M}^{-1}$.

   (b) $\mathbf{A} = \begin{pmatrix} 1 & 7 & 4 \\ 0 & 1 & 2 \\ 0 & 0 & 1 \end{pmatrix}$, $\mathbf{B} = \begin{pmatrix} 1 & 0 & 0 \\ 3 & 1 & 0 \\ -1 & -4 & 1 \end{pmatrix}$ and $\mathbf{C} = \mathbf{AB}$.

   (i) Evaluate the matrix $\mathbf{C}$.

   (ii) Work out the matrix product $\mathbf{A}\begin{pmatrix} 1 & a & b \\ 0 & 1 & c \\ 0 & 0 & 1 \end{pmatrix}$.

   (iii) By equating the product in part (ii) to $\begin{pmatrix} 1 & 0 & 0 \\ 0 & 1 & 0 \\ 0 & 0 & 1 \end{pmatrix}$, find $\mathbf{A}^{-1}$.

   (iv) Using a similar method, or otherwise, find $\mathbf{B}^{-1}$.

   (v) Using your results from part (iii) and (iv), find $\mathbf{C}^{-1}$. **[MEI 1993]**

Exercise 4C continued

13. The one–way stretch S, $\times 5$ parallel to the line $y = \frac{1}{2}x$ may be accomplished by

(i) rotating the plane clockwise through the angle $\arctan(\frac{1}{2})$ about O, and then

(ii) doing a one–way stretch, $\times 5$ parallel to the x axis, and then

(iii) rotating the plane anticlockwise through the angle $\arctan(\frac{1}{2})$ about O.

(a) Find the matrix for each of the transformations described in (i), (ii) and (iii), and hence find the matrix which represents S.

(b) Transformation S maps figure F to F'. Describe the transformation which maps F' to F and find its matrix.

14. The 2×2 matrix $\mathbf{Z} = \begin{pmatrix} a & c \\ b & d \end{pmatrix}$ is such that $\mathbf{Z}^2$ is the 2×2 zero matrix.

(i) Show that $\mathbf{Z}$ can be expressed in terms of a and b only, or in terms of either b or c only.

(ii) Show that when $\mathbf{Z}$ can be expressed in terms of b only, we can write $\mathbf{Z} = \mathbf{ERP}$, where

$$\mathbf{E} = \begin{pmatrix} b & 0 \\ 0 & b \end{pmatrix} \qquad \mathbf{R} = \begin{pmatrix} 0 & -1 \\ 1 & 0 \end{pmatrix} \qquad \mathbf{P} = \begin{pmatrix} 1 & 0 \\ 0 & 0 \end{pmatrix}$$

(iii) Describe the transformations represented by matrices $\mathbf{E}$, $\mathbf{R}$ and $\mathbf{P}$.

(iv) Explain how this fits the fact that $\mathbf{Z}^2$ is the zero matrix.

15. A 2×2 matrix $\mathbf{A}$ is such that $\mathbf{A}^2 - 4\mathbf{A} + 3\mathbf{I} = \mathbf{O}$, the zero matrix.

(i) Show that $(\mathbf{A} + 3\mathbf{I})(\mathbf{A} - 7\mathbf{I}) = k\mathbf{I}$, where k is a constant, stating the value of k. Hence describe the transformation which maps $\begin{pmatrix} x \\ y \end{pmatrix}$ to

$$(\mathbf{A} + 3\mathbf{I})(\mathbf{A} - 7\mathbf{I})\begin{pmatrix} x \\ y \end{pmatrix}.$$

(ii) Prove that $(\mathbf{A} - 2\mathbf{I})$ is its own inverse.

(iii) Show that the matrix $\begin{pmatrix} -3 & -4 \\ 6 & 7 \end{pmatrix}$ satisfies the equation $\mathbf{A}^2 - 4\mathbf{A} + 3\mathbf{I} = \mathbf{O}$.

[O&C 1993]

Linear transformations

Many transformations exhibit the property illustrated in the next example.

EXAMPLE Transformation T has matrix $\begin{pmatrix} 3 & 5 \\ 1 & 2 \end{pmatrix}$ and $\mathbf{p}$ and $\mathbf{q}$ are the vectors $\begin{pmatrix} x_1 \\ y_1 \end{pmatrix}$ and $\begin{pmatrix} x_2 \\ y_2 \end{pmatrix}$. Find the image of the points with position vectors $\mathbf{p}$, $\mathbf{q}$, and $\lambda\mathbf{p} + \mu\mathbf{q}$, where λ and μ are arbitrary constants, and show that

$$T(\lambda\mathbf{p} + \mu\mathbf{q}) = \lambda T(\mathbf{p}) + \mu T(\mathbf{q})$$

Solution

$$T(\mathbf{p}) = \begin{pmatrix} 3 & 5 \\ 1 & 2 \end{pmatrix}\begin{pmatrix} x_1 \\ y_1 \end{pmatrix} = \begin{pmatrix} 3x_1 + 5y_1 \\ x_1 + 2y_1 \end{pmatrix}$$

$$T(\mathbf{q}) = \begin{pmatrix} 3 & 5 \\ 1 & 2 \end{pmatrix}\begin{pmatrix} x_2 \\ y_2 \end{pmatrix} = \begin{pmatrix} 3x_2 + 5y_2 \\ x_2 + 2y_2 \end{pmatrix}$$

$$T(\lambda\mathbf{p} + \mu\mathbf{q}) = \begin{pmatrix} 3 & 5 \\ 1 & 2 \end{pmatrix}\left(\lambda\begin{pmatrix} x_1 \\ y_1 \end{pmatrix} + \mu\begin{pmatrix} x_2 \\ y_2 \end{pmatrix} \right)$$

$$= \begin{pmatrix} 3(\lambda x_1 + \mu x_2) + 5(\lambda y_1 + \mu y_2) \\ (\lambda x_1 + \mu x_2) + 2(\lambda y_1 + \mu y_2) \end{pmatrix}$$

$$= \begin{pmatrix} \lambda(3x_1 + 5y_1) + \mu(3x_2 + 5y_2) \\ \lambda(x_1 + 2y_1) + \mu(x_2 + 2y_2) \end{pmatrix}$$

$$= \lambda\begin{pmatrix} 3x_1 + 5y_1 \\ x_1 + 2y_1 \end{pmatrix} + \mu\begin{pmatrix} 3x_2 + 5y_2 \\ x_2 + 2y_2 \end{pmatrix}$$

Thus $T(\lambda\mathbf{p} + \mu\mathbf{q}) = \lambda T(\mathbf{p}) + \mu\, T(\mathbf{q})$.

Any transformation T which has the property that

$$T(\lambda\mathbf{p} + \mu\mathbf{q}) = \lambda T(\mathbf{p}) + \mu T(\mathbf{q})$$

whatever the scalars λ and μ, and whatever the vectors $\mathbf{p}$ and $\mathbf{q}$, is known as a *linear transformation*.

Work exactly similar to that above shows that whenever we can specify a transformation T by means of a matrix $\mathbf{M}$, so that the point P with position vector $\mathbf{p}$ maps to P' with position vector $T(\mathbf{p}) = \mathbf{p}' = \mathbf{Mp}$, then

$$T(\lambda\mathbf{p} + \mu\mathbf{q}) = \lambda T(\mathbf{p}) + \mu T(\mathbf{q})$$

for all λ and μ, and for all $\mathbf{p}$ and $\mathbf{q}$. This means that all transformations that can be represented in this way by matrices are linear transformations.

Activity

By writing **p** as **p** + **0** show that a linear transformation always maps the origin to the origin. Why is a non–zero translation not a linear transformation?

Perhaps surprisingly, if T is a linear transformation mapping **p** to **p′**, it can be represented by a matrix **M** in such a way that **p′** = **Mp**. The order of **M** depends on the dimensions of both the domain and the co-domain of T. Suppose, for example, T is a linear transformation mapping (x, y) to $(x′, y′)$ in such a way that $T(\mathbf{i}) = \begin{pmatrix} 3 \\ 2 \end{pmatrix}$ and $T(\mathbf{j}) = \begin{pmatrix} 0 \\ 4 \end{pmatrix}$. Then applying the definition of a linear transformation to T gives

$$T(x\mathbf{i} + y\mathbf{j}) = xT(\mathbf{i}) + yT(\mathbf{j})$$

$$= x\begin{pmatrix} 3 \\ 2 \end{pmatrix} + y\begin{pmatrix} 0 \\ 4 \end{pmatrix}$$

$$= \begin{pmatrix} 3x \\ 2x + 4y \end{pmatrix}$$

$$= \mathbf{M}\begin{pmatrix} x \\ y \end{pmatrix} \quad \text{where } \mathbf{M} = \begin{pmatrix} 3 & 0 \\ 2 & 4 \end{pmatrix}$$

A similar proof applies in the general case.

Linear transformations preserve linearity

We now prove that, under a linear transformation, the image of a line is a line. In other words, linear transformations preserve linearity. Consider the line with equation **r** = **a** + λ**d**. Then, under transformation T, the image of R is R′, with position vector

$$\mathbf{r′} = T(\mathbf{r}) = T(\mathbf{a} + \lambda\mathbf{d})$$

$$= T(\mathbf{a}) + \lambda T(\mathbf{d}) \quad \text{since } T \text{ is a linear transformation}$$

Thus **r′** = **a′** + λ**d′**, which is the equation of a straight line, provided (for the moment) that **d′** ≠ **0**.

EXAMPLE

Find the image of the line l with equation $y = 2x + 3$ under the transformation T with matrix $\begin{pmatrix} 2 & 3 \\ 5 & 1 \end{pmatrix}$.

Solution 1

As T is a linear transformation, it preserves linearity, so we can find the image of l by first finding the image of any two points on l.

A (0, 3) is on l. $T(\mathbf{A})$ has position vector $\begin{pmatrix} 2 & 3 \\ 5 & 1 \end{pmatrix}\begin{pmatrix} 0 \\ 3 \end{pmatrix} = \begin{pmatrix} 9 \\ 3 \end{pmatrix}$.

B (2, 7) is on l. $T(\mathbf{B})$ has position vector $\begin{pmatrix} 2 & 3 \\ 5 & 1 \end{pmatrix}\begin{pmatrix} 2 \\ 7 \end{pmatrix} = \begin{pmatrix} 25 \\ 17 \end{pmatrix}$.

The equation of the line passing through $(9, 3)$ and $(25, 17)$ is

$$y - 3 = \frac{17 - 3}{25 - 9}(x - 9)$$

$$\Rightarrow \quad y - 3 = \tfrac{7}{8}(x - 9)$$

$$\Rightarrow \quad 8y - 24 = 7x - 63$$

$$\Rightarrow \quad 7x - 8y = 39$$

Solution 2

The general point on the line $y = 2x + 3$ is $(t, 2t + 3)$. Its image (x', y') under T is given by

$$\begin{pmatrix} x' \\ y' \end{pmatrix} = \begin{pmatrix} 2 & 3 \\ 5 & 1 \end{pmatrix}\begin{pmatrix} t \\ 2t + 3 \end{pmatrix} = \begin{pmatrix} 8t + 9 \\ 7t + 3 \end{pmatrix}$$

Eliminating t from the equations

$$\begin{cases} x' = 8t + 9 \\ y' = 7t + 3 \end{cases}$$ gives $7x' - 8y' = 39$ so the image line has equation $7x - 8y = 39$.

Exercise 4D

1. Which of the following are linear transformations?

(a) Reflection in $y = x$.

(b) Reflection in $y = x - 1$.

(c) Half turn about $(2, 0)$.

(d) A positive quarter turn about $(0, 0)$.

(e) The shear with matrix $\begin{pmatrix} 1 & 2 \\ 0 & 1 \end{pmatrix}$.

(f) Enlargement, scale factor 2, centre $(2, 1)$.

2. Transformation T is a projection. Each point is mapped on to ℓ, the line $y = 2x$. The line joining each point to its image is perpendicular to ℓ. Find the co-ordinates of the image of the point (p, q). Is T a linear transformation? Justify your decision.

3. Explain what is meant by the statement 'T is a linear transformation'. If T maps (x, y) to $(|x|, y)$ is T a linear transformation? Use your definition to justify your answer.

4. A linear transformation maps distinct points A and B to A' and B'. Show that

(i) A' and B' are distinct $\Rightarrow$ all points on line AB map to points on line A'B';

(ii) A' and B' coincide $\Rightarrow$ all points on line AB map to A'.

5. Prove that under a linear transformation the images of parallel lines are parallel lines, and hence that the co-ordinate grid of unit squares maps into a grid of congruent parallelograms.

6. *T* is a linear transformation and the point C divides AB in the ratio *m* : *n*. Express **c** in terms of **a** and **b** and hence deduce that *T*(C) divides *T*(AB) in the ratio *m* : *n*.

7. The centroid of any triangle ABC is the point with position vector $\frac{1}{3}(\mathbf{a} + \mathbf{b} + \mathbf{c})$. The linear transformation *T* maps A, B, C to A′, B′, C′ respectively. If G is the centroid of triangle ABC, show that *T*(G) is the centroid of triangle A′B′C′.

8. Some textbooks define *T* as a linear transformation if
(i) $T(k\mathbf{u}) = kT(\mathbf{u})$
and (ii) $T(\mathbf{u} + \mathbf{v}) = T(\mathbf{u}) + T(\mathbf{v})$,
whatever the number *k* and whatever the vectors **u** and **v**. Show that this definition is equivalent to the one we have given.

9. (i) A transformation *T* maps the point P(*x*, *y*) to P′(*x*′, *y*′), where *x*′ and *y*′ are given by $\begin{pmatrix} x' \\ y' \\ 1 \end{pmatrix} = \begin{pmatrix} 1 & 0 & 3 \\ 0 & 1 & -5 \\ 0 & 0 & 1 \end{pmatrix} \begin{pmatrix} x \\ y \\ 1 \end{pmatrix}$. Is *T* a linear transformation?

Justify your answer and describe the transformation as simply as possible.

(ii) Find a similar matrix method of representing a 90° anticlockwise rotation about the point (2, 1). Is this a linear transformation?

10. Quadratic functions may be represented by points in three-dimensional space as follows: the point (*a*, *b*, *c*) represents $ax^2 + bx + c$. In a similar way we may represent linear functions by points in two-dimensional space. Show that differentiating quadratic functions may be regarded as a linear transformation, and find the matrix which represents differentiation of fourth-degree polynomials.

Determinants of 2 × 2 matrices

On page 99 we defined the determinant of the 2 × 2 matrix $\mathbf{M} = \begin{pmatrix} a & c \\ b & d \end{pmatrix}$

as the number $ad - bc$. It is denoted in several ways: det **M**, |**M**|, or $\begin{vmatrix} a & c \\ b & d \end{vmatrix}$.

We now look at its significance.

Activity

(i) The diagram shows the unit square and its image under *T*, defined by

Activity continued

matrix $T = \begin{pmatrix} 3 & 1 \\ 1 & 2 \end{pmatrix}$. Explain why the image is a parallelogram, find its area and evaluate det **T**.

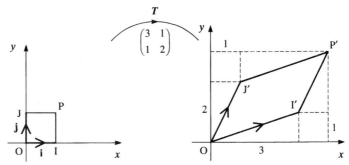

(ii) Transformations R and S are defined by the matrices $R = \begin{pmatrix} 3 & 5 \\ 1 & 1 \end{pmatrix}$

and $S = \begin{pmatrix} 3 & 6 \\ 1 & 2 \end{pmatrix}$. Apply R and S to the unit square. Find the area of the images, and evaluate det R and det S.

(iii) Comment on what you notice.

Ignoring (for the moment) the sign of the determinant, you will have found that the determinant is the area scale factor for the transformation. If you move anticlockwise around the original shape (the unit square) you come to the vertices O, I, P, J, in that order; moving around the images in the same order you are again moving anticlockwise in (i), but you are moving clockwise in (ii). It is this reversal of *sense* that is indicated by the negative sign of det **R** in (ii).

Activity

The diagram shows rectangle PQRS with horizontal and vertical sides of lengths h, k respectively, together with its image P'Q'R'S' under T, defined

by matrix $T = \begin{pmatrix} a & c \\ b & d \end{pmatrix}$. You may assume that det T is positive.

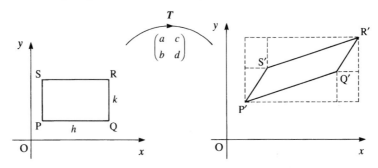

Activity continued

Show that $\overrightarrow{P'Q'} = \begin{pmatrix} ha \\ hb \end{pmatrix}$. Find $\overrightarrow{P'S'}$ and deduce that the area of P'Q'R'S' is

area of PQRS × det **T**.

The area of any plane shape can be found as accurately as we wish as the sum of a number of sufficiently small squares. When a shape is

transformed by *T*, with matrix $\mathbf{T} = \begin{pmatrix} a & c \\ b & d \end{pmatrix}$, the area of each of these squares

is multiplied by the same scale factor, det $\mathbf{T} = ad - bc$. Thus $ad - bc$ is the area scale factor for the transformation. Strictly we should say that det $\mathbf{T} = ad - bc$ is the *signed* area scale factor, as it can be negative, signifying that the sense (clockwise or anticlockwise) has been reversed.

Activity

M is the matrix representing reflection of the plane in the line $y = x \tan \theta$. Show that det **M** = −1 and draw a diagram to demonstrate that vertices labelled clockwise around a shape are transformed to vertices labelled anticlockwise around the image.

For Discussion

Find several 2 × 2 matrices whose determinants are 0. Apply the transformations corresponding to your matrices to shapes of your own choice. What do you notice?

If det **T** = 0 the matrix **T** is said to be *singular*, and the transformation

represented by $\mathbf{T} = \begin{pmatrix} a & c \\ b & d \end{pmatrix}$ maps the whole plane on to a single line P'Q'

(which passes through the origin, as shown in figure 4.9) or on to a single

point (which has to be the origin, and that only happens if $\mathbf{T} = \begin{pmatrix} 0 & 0 \\ 0 & 0 \end{pmatrix}$,

the zero matrix). Each point in the range (i.e. each point on line P'Q') is the image of infinitely many points in the domain. All the points which map to P' fall on a straight line, labelled AB in figure 4.9, and every point on AB

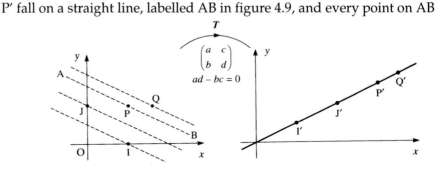

Figure 4.9

maps to P'. I' is also the image of all points on a line through I parallel to AB. Each point on a line through Q parallel to AB maps to Q'.

Activity

Prove that the general point $P(x, y)$ maps to P' on the line $bx - ay = 0$ when the plane is transformed using the matrix $\begin{pmatrix} a & c \\ b & d \end{pmatrix}$, where $ad - bc = 0$.

We now prove that if det $\mathbf{M} \neq 0$, distinct points A, B will have distinct images, A', B' under the transformation represented by $\mathbf{M}$. To do this consider a third point C not on line AB. Then triangle ABC has non-zero area, S say. We have proved earlier that the area of the image triangle A'B'C' is $S \times$ det $\mathbf{M}$, which is not zero as neither S nor det $\mathbf{M}$ is zero. We conclude, therefore, that A', B', C' are distinct points (and not on the same straight line).

Exercise 4E

1. Find the values of the determinants of the following matrices and decide whether the matrices are singular or non-singular.

   (a) $\begin{pmatrix} 6 & 4 \\ 2 & 3 \end{pmatrix}$ (b) $\begin{pmatrix} 4 & 8 \\ -1 & -2 \end{pmatrix}$ (c) $\begin{pmatrix} 5 & 3 \\ 1 & \frac{3}{5} \end{pmatrix}$ (d) $\begin{pmatrix} 1 & -2 \\ 2 & 3 \end{pmatrix}$

2. Show that the determinant of the matrix representing rotation of the plane through angle α anticlockwise about the origin is 1.

3. By considering the significance of the determinant, explain why det$(\mathbf{MN})$ = det $\mathbf{M} \times$ det $\mathbf{N}$, and check the result numerically using 2×2 matrices $\mathbf{M}$ and $\mathbf{N}$ of your own choice.

4. The two–way stretch with matrix $\begin{pmatrix} a & 0 \\ 0 & d \end{pmatrix}$ preserves area. What is the relationship connecting a and d?

5. The point P is projected to P' on the line $3y = x$, so that PP' is parallel to $y = 3x$. Find the image of the point (s, t) and hence find the matrix representing this transformation. Show that the determinant of the matrix is 0.

6. The plane is transformed by means of the matrix $\mathbf{M} = \begin{pmatrix} 2 & 4 \\ 1 & 2 \end{pmatrix}$.

   (i) Show that det $\mathbf{M} = 0$, and that the whole plane is mapped onto the line $x - 2y = 0$.

   (ii) The point P (x, y) is mapped to P' $(4, 2)$. Use the equation $\mathbf{p}' = \mathbf{Mp}$ to show that P could be any point on the line $x + 2y = 2$.

   (iii) Find the equation of the line of points that map to $(10, 5)$.

Exercise 4E continued

7. The points P, Q and R have co-ordinates (x_p, y_p), (x_q, y_q) and (x_r, y_r) respectively. Show that the area of triangle OPQ is $\pm\dfrac{1}{2}\begin{vmatrix} x_p & x_q \\ y_p & y_q \end{vmatrix}$.

Hence show that the area of triangle PQR is $\pm\dfrac{1}{2}\begin{vmatrix} x_p - x_r & x_q - x_r \\ y_p - y_r & y_q - y_r \end{vmatrix}$.

8. Shear S moves each point parallel to the fixed line $y = x \tan \alpha$. Each point moves k times its distance from the fixed line. Show that the matrix for this transformation is $\begin{pmatrix} 1 + k \sin \alpha \cos \alpha & -k \cos^2 \alpha \\ k \sin^2 \alpha & 1 - k \sin \alpha \cos \alpha \end{pmatrix}$

and hence show that shears preserve area.

9. The equations $\begin{cases} a_1 x + b_1 y = c_1 \\ a_2 x + b_2 y = c_2 \end{cases}$ may be written as $x\mathbf{a} + y\mathbf{b} = \mathbf{c}$, where

$\mathbf{a} = \begin{pmatrix} a_1 \\ a_2 \end{pmatrix}$ etc. Show that the solution is $x = \dfrac{\begin{vmatrix} \mathbf{c} & \mathbf{b} \end{vmatrix}}{\begin{vmatrix} \mathbf{a} & \mathbf{b} \end{vmatrix}}$, $y = \dfrac{\begin{vmatrix} \mathbf{a} & \mathbf{c} \end{vmatrix}}{\begin{vmatrix} \mathbf{a} & \mathbf{b} \end{vmatrix}}$ where $\begin{vmatrix} \mathbf{a} & \mathbf{b} \end{vmatrix}$

stands for $\begin{vmatrix} a_1 & b_1 \\ a_2 & b_2 \end{vmatrix}$, the determinant of the matrix $\begin{pmatrix} a_1 & b_1 \\ a_2 & b_2 \end{pmatrix}$ etc.

Note particularly the positions of $\mathbf{c}$ in the determinant in the numerators of the expressions for x and y. (This is the 2×2 version of what is known as *Cramer's rule*, first published by Gabriel Cramer in 1750 though it appears to have been known by Maclaurin as early as 1729).

Matrices and simultaneous equations

Solving the simultaneous equations $\begin{cases} x' = ax + cy : \\ y' = bx + dy \end{cases}$ may be regarded as

solving the matrix equation: $\mathbf{M}\begin{pmatrix} x \\ y \end{pmatrix} = \begin{pmatrix} e \\ f \end{pmatrix}$, where $\mathbf{M} = \begin{pmatrix} a & c \\ b & d \end{pmatrix}$. If det $\mathbf{M} \neq 0$,

$\mathbf{M}^{-1}$ exists, and pre-multiplying both sides by $\mathbf{M}^{-1}$ gives

$$\mathbf{M}^{-1}\mathbf{M}\begin{pmatrix} x \\ y \end{pmatrix} = \mathbf{M}^{-1}\begin{pmatrix} e \\ f \end{pmatrix}$$

$$\Rightarrow \quad \begin{pmatrix} x \\ y \end{pmatrix} = \mathbf{M}^{-1}\begin{pmatrix} e \\ f \end{pmatrix}$$

EXAMPLE

Solve the equations $\begin{cases} 3x + 2y = 9 \\ 4x + 5y = 5 \end{cases}$ simultaneously.

Solution

The equations may be rewritten as the single matrix equation

$$\begin{pmatrix} 3 & 2 \\ 4 & 5 \end{pmatrix}\begin{pmatrix} x \\ y \end{pmatrix} = \begin{pmatrix} 9 \\ 5 \end{pmatrix}$$

We pre-multiply both sides by $\begin{pmatrix} 3 & 2 \\ 4 & 5 \end{pmatrix}^{-1} = \dfrac{1}{7}\begin{pmatrix} 5 & -2 \\ -4 & 3 \end{pmatrix}$ getting

$$\frac{1}{7}\begin{pmatrix} 5 & -2 \\ -4 & 3 \end{pmatrix}\begin{pmatrix} 3 & 2 \\ 4 & 5 \end{pmatrix}\begin{pmatrix} x \\ y \end{pmatrix} = \frac{1}{7}\begin{pmatrix} 5 & -2 \\ -4 & 3 \end{pmatrix}\begin{pmatrix} 9 \\ 5 \end{pmatrix}$$

As $\mathbf{M}^{-1}\mathbf{Mp} = \mathbf{p}$, the left-hand side simplifies to $\begin{pmatrix} x \\ y \end{pmatrix}$, giving

$$\begin{pmatrix} x \\ y \end{pmatrix} = \frac{1}{7}\begin{pmatrix} 35 \\ -21 \end{pmatrix}$$

The solution is $x = 5$, $y = -3$.

Solving the simultaneous equations $\begin{cases} x' = ax + cy \\ y' = bx + dy \end{cases}$ may be interpreted in two ways.

Interpretation A

The two equations may be regarded as the equations of two lines in a plane. We are looking for points common to both lines. The two lines may

(a) cross, at a single common point, as shown in figure 4.10: the equations have a unique solution;

or

Figure 4.10

(b) have no common points because they are distinct parallel lines, as shown in figure 4.11: the equations have no solution and we say that the equations are *inconsistent*;

or

Figure 4.11

(c) be coincident lines, having all their points in common, as shown in figure 4.12: the equations have infinitely many solutions, which may be expressed in terms of a single parameter.

Figure 4.12

Interpretation B

We are dealing with a transformation of the plane, with matrix **M**. We are given that the co-ordinates of P' are (e, f) and we are looking for the co-ordinates of P, the point that is mapped to P'. Either det $\mathbf{M} \neq 0$, as described in (a) below, or det $\mathbf{M} = 0$, giving rise to situations (b) or (c) below.

(a) If det $\mathbf{M} \neq 0$, **M** is non-singular, $\mathbf{M}^{-1}$ exists, and there is a unique position for P, as shown in figure 4.13, and a unique solution to the equations.

Figure 4.13

If det $\mathbf{M} = 0$, **M** is singular, $\mathbf{M}^{-1}$ does not exist, and the transformation maps all points on to a single line ℓ (through the origin); whether we have a solution or not depends on whether P' is on ℓ or not.

(b) If P' is not on ℓ, then P' is not the image of any point: the equations have no solutions; the equations are inconsistent (figure 4.14).

Figure 4.14

(c) If P' is on ℓ, then there are infinitely many possible positions for P, all the points on a certain line (figure 4.15): the equations have infinitely many solutions, which may be expressed in terms of a single parameter.

Figure 4.15

Throughout Interpretation B we have assumed that **M** is not the zero matrix, a trivial and obvious situation in which all points of the plane are mapped to the origin. There will be no solution if P' is not at the origin. If P' is at the origin, P may be anywhere on the plane: x and y may take any values.

Similarly the three simultaneous equations in three variables

$$a_1 x + b_1 y + c_1 z = d_1$$
$$a_2 x + b_2 y + c_2 z = d_2$$
$$a_3 x + b_3 y + c_3 z = d_3$$

are equivalent to the matrix equation $\mathbf{M} \begin{pmatrix} x \\ y \\ z \end{pmatrix} = \begin{pmatrix} d_1 \\ d_2 \\ d_3 \end{pmatrix}$, where $\mathbf{M} = \begin{pmatrix} a_1 & b_1 & c_1 \\ a_2 & b_2 & c_2 \\ a_3 & b_3 & c_3 \end{pmatrix}$.

The three equations may be regarded as the equations of three planes in three-dimensional space. There are seven possible configurations.

(a) If det $\mathbf{M} \neq 0$, $\mathbf{M}$ is non–singular, $\mathbf{M}^{-1}$ exists, and the equations have a unique solution. This corresponds to the three planes having a single common point, figure 4.16.

Figure 4.16

If det $\mathbf{M} = 0$, $\mathbf{M}$ is singular and $\mathbf{M}^{-1}$ does not exist: in this case either the equations are inconsistent and have no solutions, see (b) below; or the equations have infinitely many solutions, see (c) below.

(b) The equations being inconsistent and having no solutions corresponds to the three planes having no common points. When this happens

    (i) the three planes form a triangular prism, figure 4.17;

    or

Figure 4.17

    (ii) two planes are parallel and distinct, and crossed by the third plane, figure 4.18;

    or

Figure 4.18

    (iii) two planes are coincident and the third plane is parallel but distinct, figure 4.19;

    or

Figure 4.19

    (iv) all three planes are parallel and distinct, figure 4.20.

Figure 4.20

(c) The equations having infinitely many solutions correspond to the three planes having infinitely many common points. When this happens

either

(i) the three planes have a line of common points: this arrangement is known as a *sheaf* or *pencil* of planes, figure 4.21; the solutions are given in terms of a single parameter;

or

Figure 4.21

(ii) the three planes all coincide, figure 4.22: the solutions are given in terms of two parameters.

Figure 4.22

Again we have ignored the trivial situation where **M** consists entirely of zeros. Figure 4.23 summarises the decisions that need to be made.

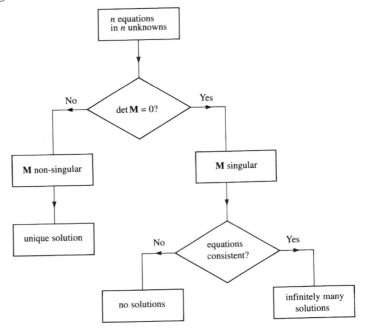

Figure 4.23

EXAMPLE

Investigate the solution of the equations $\begin{cases} x + 3y - 2z = 7 & A \\ 2x - 2y + z = 3 & B \\ 3x + y - z = k & C \end{cases}$

(i) when $k = 10$; (ii) when $k = 12$.

Solution

We start by eliminating one variable (z) to obtain two equations in x, y.

$$A - 2C: \quad -5x + y = 7 - 2k \quad \Rightarrow \quad 5x - y = -7 + 2k$$

$$B + C: \quad 5x - y = 3 + k$$

Now $5x - y$ can only equal $-7 + 2k$ and $3 + k$ if

$$-7 + 2k = 3 + k$$

$$\Leftrightarrow \quad k = 10$$

(i) When $k = 10$, equations $A - 2C$ and $B + C$ both reduce to $5x - y = 13$, so we can only solve for x and y (and later z) in terms of a parameter.

If $x = \lambda$, $y = 5\lambda - 13$ and from equation C we get

$$z = 3\lambda + 5\lambda - 13 - 10 = 8\lambda - 23$$

We have a line of solution points, which can be given in terms of a single parameter: $(\lambda, 5\lambda - 13, 8\lambda - 23)$. The three planes are arranged as a sheaf.

(ii) When $k = 12$, equations $A - 2C$ and $B + C$ are inconsistent as $5x - y$ cannot be both 17 and 15.

Equations A and B are the same as in (i), so the corresponding planes have not changed. In equation C the value of k has changed from 10 to 12, causing a translation of the plane.

The original equations are inconsistent. The corresponding planes form a triangular prism.

Alternative approaches

We show how to evaluate a 3×3 determinant on page 157. However, a calculator tells us that $\begin{vmatrix} 1 & 3 & -2 \\ 2 & -2 & 1 \\ 3 & 1 & -1 \end{vmatrix} = 0$, so we know that we do not have a unique solution but either no solutions or many solutions.

The normals corresponding to the equations A, B, C are clearly not parallel, so our three planes are not parallel (or identical): we can only be dealing with a sheaf of planes or a triangular prism.

Examination of the equations shows that $C = A + B$ when $k = 10$, so that the equations are not inconsistent in (i) and we then have a sheaf of planes, their common line being the line of solution points. (If we want to find expressions for these points we can use algebraic methods, as in the first solution, or use vector methods, as explained in Chapter 5.)

As before, changing the value of k translates the plane represented by C, but does not affect the other two planes so in (ii) the three planes form a triangular prism and the equations are inconsistent.

Exercise 4F

In Questions 1 – 10 decide whether the equations are consistent or inconsistent. If they are consistent, solve them, in terms of a parameter if necessary. In each question also describe the configuration of the corresponding lines or planes.

1. $\begin{aligned} 3x + 5y &= 17 \\ 2x + 4y &= 11 \end{aligned}$
2. $\begin{aligned} 3x + 6y &= 12 \\ 2x + 4y &= 15 \end{aligned}$
3. $\begin{aligned} 6x - 3y &= 12 \\ 2x - y &= 4 \end{aligned}$
4. $\begin{aligned} 8x - 4y &= 11 \\ y &= 2x - 4 \end{aligned}$

5. $\begin{aligned} x + y + z &= 4 \\ 2x + 3y - 4z &= 3 \\ 5x + 8y - 13z &= 8 \end{aligned}$
6. $\begin{aligned} 2x - y &= 1 \\ 3x + 2z &= 13 \\ 3y + 4z &= 23 \end{aligned}$
7. $\begin{aligned} x + 2y + 4z &= 7 \\ 3x + 2y + 5z &= 21 \\ 4x + y + 2z &= 14 \end{aligned}$

8. $\begin{aligned} 3x + 2y + z &= 2 \\ 5x + 3y - 4z &= 1 \\ x + y + 4z &= 5 \end{aligned}$
9. $\begin{aligned} 2x + y - z &= 5 \\ 8x + 4y - 4z &= 20 \\ -2x - y + z &= -5 \end{aligned}$
10. $\begin{aligned} 5x + 3y - 2z &= 6 \\ 6x + 2y + 3z &= 11 \\ 7x + y + 8z &= 12 \end{aligned}$

11. Find the two values of k for which the equations $\begin{cases} 2x + ky = 3 \\ kx + 8y = 6 \end{cases}$

do not have a unique solution. In both cases find the solution set for the equations.

12. Given that det $\mathbf{M} = 0$, where $\mathbf{M}$ is a 2×2 matrix, explain why

$\mathbf{M} \begin{pmatrix} x \\ y \end{pmatrix} = \begin{pmatrix} p \\ q \end{pmatrix}$ has infinitely many solutions if both p and q are zero.

What happens if p and q are not both zero?

13. Solve the equation $\begin{pmatrix} 1 & 3 & -2 \\ -3 & 1 & 1 \\ -3 & 11 & -4 \end{pmatrix} \begin{pmatrix} x \\ y \\ z \end{pmatrix} = \begin{pmatrix} -2 \\ 6 \\ k \end{pmatrix}$ in each of the two cases

(i) $k = 3$, and (ii) $k = 6$, giving x, y and z in terms of a parameter λ if appropriate. In both cases interpret your solution geometrically with reference to three appropriate planes.

14. A is a 3×3 matrix and d is a 3×1 column vector. Show that all solutions of the equation $\mathbf{Ar} = \mathbf{d}$ can be expressed in the form $\mathbf{r} = \mathbf{p} + \mathbf{k}$, where $\mathbf{p}$ is any particular solution (of $\mathbf{Ar} = \mathbf{d}$) and $\mathbf{k}$ is any solution of the related equation $\mathbf{Ar} = \mathbf{0}$. Does it matter if A is singular or non-singular? (If you are studying Mechanics 4 you should compare what we have just done with the solution of linear differential equations by the method of particular integral and complementary function.)

15. Show that the equations $\begin{cases} 3x + 2y = 4 \\ 2x - 3y = 7 \\ 5x - 4y = k \end{cases}$ are inconsistent unless k

takes one particular value, which you should state.

Invariance

Invariant points

In any rotation, the centre C of the rotation maps to itself (figure 4.24). C is an example of an *invariant point*. In a reflection, points on the mirror line do not move – a further example of invariant points.

Figure 4.24

The product $\begin{pmatrix} 6 & 5 \\ 2 & 3 \end{pmatrix}\begin{pmatrix} 2 \\ -2 \end{pmatrix} = \begin{pmatrix} 2 \\ -2 \end{pmatrix}$. This means that the

transformation with matrix $\begin{pmatrix} 6 & 5 \\ 2 & 3 \end{pmatrix}$ maps the point

$(2, -2)$ to itself. This is another example of an invariant point.

Activity

Explain why the origin is always an invariant point in a linear transformation.

EXAMPLE

Find the invariant points under the transformation given by the matrix $\begin{pmatrix} 2 & -1 \\ 1 & 0 \end{pmatrix}$.

Solution

Suppose $\begin{pmatrix} x \\ y \end{pmatrix}$ maps to itself. Then

$$\begin{pmatrix} 2 & -1 \\ 1 & 0 \end{pmatrix}\begin{pmatrix} x \\ y \end{pmatrix} = \begin{pmatrix} x \\ y \end{pmatrix}$$

$$\Leftrightarrow \quad \begin{pmatrix} 2x - y \\ x \end{pmatrix} = \begin{pmatrix} x \\ y \end{pmatrix}$$

$$\Leftrightarrow \quad 2x - y = x \quad \text{and} \quad x = y$$

$$\Leftrightarrow \quad x = y$$

Thus all points on the line $y = x$ (and only points on this line) map on to themselves. This is a line of invariant points. (It is also an example of an invariant line.)

Invariant lines

The line AB is known as an *invariant line* under *T* if the image of each point on AB is on AB. It is important to note that it is not necessary for points on AB to map on to themselves (as in the example above), but merely that each point on AB maps to a point on AB.

Occasionally it is easy to spot which lines are invariant: for example, in a reflection, as well as the mirror line being invariant (because it is a line of invariant points), each line perpendicular to the mirror line is invariant, as illustrated in figure 4.25. Because the mirror line is a line of invariant points it is sometimes described as 'pointwise invariant'.

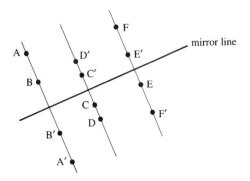

Figure 4.25

The following examples illustrate the usual methods of identifying invariant lines.

EXAMPLE

A transformation is defined by the matrix $\begin{pmatrix} 3 & 2 \\ 1 & 2 \end{pmatrix}$. Find the invariant lines which pass through the origin, and illustrate the transformation diagramatically.

Solution

Consider a general point on the line $y = mx$, such as $\begin{pmatrix} X \\ mX \end{pmatrix}$.

This maps to $\begin{pmatrix} 3 & 2 \\ 1 & 2 \end{pmatrix}\begin{pmatrix} X \\ mX \end{pmatrix} = \begin{pmatrix} 3X + 2mX \\ X + 2mX \end{pmatrix}$ and we want this image to be a point on the same line, $y = mx$, so

$$X + 2mX = m(3X + 2mX)$$
$$\Leftrightarrow \quad X(2m^2 + m - 1) = 0$$

We want this to hold for all values of X, so $2m^2 + m - 1 = 0$

$$\Leftrightarrow \quad (2m - 1)(m + 1) = 0$$
$$\Leftrightarrow \quad m = \tfrac{1}{2} \text{ or } m = -1$$

Using these values of m, the invariant lines are $y = \tfrac{1}{2}x$ and $x + y = 0$.

But $y = mx$ and $\begin{pmatrix} X \\ mX \end{pmatrix}$ do not cover all possible lines through the origin: we also need to consider the vertical line $x = 0$. The general point on this line is $(0, Y)$. The image of this point is $(2Y, 2Y)$, which is not on the line $x = 0$ (unless $Y = 0$), so we conclude that the vertical line through the origin is not invariant under this transformation.

The transformation is illustrated in the digram, where the pecked lines are the invariant lines $y = \frac{1}{2}x$ and $x + y = 0$, with the latter being pointwise invariant, a line of invariant points.

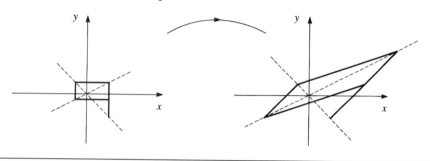

EXAMPLE

A transformation is defined by the matrix $\begin{pmatrix} 2 & -1 \\ 1 & 0 \end{pmatrix}$. Find the invariant lines.

Solution

Consider a general point on the line $y = mx + c$, such as $\begin{pmatrix} X \\ mX + c \end{pmatrix}$.

This maps to $\begin{pmatrix} 2 & -1 \\ 1 & 0 \end{pmatrix}\begin{pmatrix} X \\ mX + c \end{pmatrix} = \begin{pmatrix} 2X - mX - c \\ X \end{pmatrix}$ and we want this image to be a point on the same line, $y = mx + c$, so

$$X = m(2X - mX - c) + c$$
$$\Leftrightarrow \quad X(m^2 - 2m + 1) = c(1 - m) \qquad ①$$

This is to hold for all values of X, so

$$m^2 - 2m + 1 = c(1 - m) = 0$$
$$\Leftrightarrow \quad (1 - m)^2 = c(1 - m) = 0 \qquad ②$$

so that $m = 1$.

From ②: when $m = 1$, c may take any value.

All lines with gradient 1 are invariant, but the line $y = x$ is a line of invariant points. The diagram on page 128 shows what is happening.

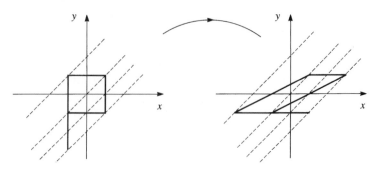

The analysis above deals with all lines except vertical ones. It is clear from the diagram that no vertical line remains invariant, or it may be proved algebraically as in the previous example.

The transformation is a shear parallel to $y = x$ and all lines parallel to $y = x$ are invariant.

A first glance at equation ① in the above example suggests we are attempting to solve a single equation in three unknowns. But we want this relationship to hold for all values of X: in effect we can construct equations in m and c by choosing values of X.

EXAMPLE Find the invariant lines of the transformation with matrix $\begin{pmatrix} 0.2 & 0.4 \\ 0.4 & 0.8 \end{pmatrix}$.

Solution

In this example the matrix is singular, and all points map on to a straight line. Consider a general point on the line $y = mx + c$, such as $\begin{pmatrix} X \\ mX + c \end{pmatrix}$.

This maps to

$$\begin{pmatrix} 0.2 & 0.4 \\ 0.4 & 0.8 \end{pmatrix} \begin{pmatrix} X \\ mX + c \end{pmatrix} = \begin{pmatrix} 0.2X + 0.4mX + 0.4c \\ 0.4X + 0.8mX + 0.8c \end{pmatrix}$$

and we want this image to be a point on the same line, $y = mx + c$, so

$$0.4X + 0.8mX + 0.8c = m(0.2X + 0.4mX + 0.4c) + c$$

$$\Leftrightarrow \quad 0.2X(2m^2 - 3m - 2) = -0.2c(1 + 2m)$$

This is to hold for all values of X, so

$$2m^2 - 3m - 2 = -0.2c(1 + 2m) = 0$$

$$\Leftrightarrow \quad (2m + 1)(m - 2) = -0.2c(1 + 2m) = 0 \qquad \qquad ①$$

so that $m = 2$ or $-\frac{1}{2}$.

From ①: $m = 2 \Rightarrow c = 0$, but when $m = -\frac{1}{2}$, c may take any value. Again a diagram is informative.

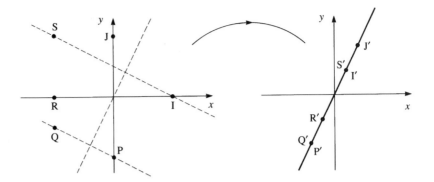

The line $y = 2x$ is invariant: it is the line to which all points are mapped in this transformation, and is in fact a line of invariant points.

The line $y = -\frac{1}{2}x + \frac{1}{2}$ passes through the point I; all points on this line map to I' (0.2, 0.4), which is itself a point on $y = -\frac{1}{2}x + \frac{1}{2}$, so the line $y = -\frac{1}{2}x + \frac{1}{2}$ is regarded as an example of an invariant line – a 'degenerate' example.

For this transformation a similar discussion applies to all lines parallel to $y = -\frac{1}{2}x + \frac{1}{2}$.

This transformation projects all points perpendicularly on to the line $y = 2x$. It is known as an *orthogonal projection*.

We need to check what happens to vertical lines. One approach is to use our understanding of what this projection does; alternatively, the general point (c, Y) on the vertical line $x = c$ maps to $(0.2c + 0.4Y, 0.4c + 0.8Y)$ which, given c, is not on $x = c$ for all values of Y. No vertical lines are invariant under this transformation.

The invariant lines are $y = 2x$ and (degenerately) all lines of the form $y = -\frac{1}{2}x + c$.

As illustrated in the previous example, it is important to note that AB is defined as invariant if each point on AB transforms to a point on AB. It is not necessary for every point on AB to be the image of a point on AB. However, these degenerate invariant lines can only occur if the determinant of the defining matrix is zero.

Activity

On page 112 we proved that under a linear transformation, the image of a line is a line. We concluded the proof with the sentence:

Thus $\mathbf{r}' = \mathbf{a}' + \lambda\mathbf{d}'$, which is the equation of a straight line, provided (for the moment) that $\mathbf{d}' \neq \mathbf{0}$.

Comment on the restriction on $\mathbf{d}'$.

Exercise 4G

In Questions 1 – 4, find the invariant points for the transformations with the given matrices.

1. $\begin{pmatrix} 0 & -1 \\ 1 & 2 \end{pmatrix}$ **2.** $\begin{pmatrix} 3 & 4 \\ 1 & 2 \end{pmatrix}$ **3.** $\begin{pmatrix} 0.6 & 0.8 \\ 0.8 & -0.6 \end{pmatrix}$ **4.** $\begin{pmatrix} \frac{1}{\sqrt{2}} & -\frac{1}{\sqrt{2}} \\ -\frac{1}{\sqrt{2}} & \frac{1}{\sqrt{2}} \end{pmatrix}$

In Questions 5 – 8 for the transformations with the given matrices find the invariant lines which pass through the origin.

5. $\begin{pmatrix} -3 & 4 \\ 4 & 3 \end{pmatrix}$ **6.** $\begin{pmatrix} 1 & 0 \\ 2 & 2 \end{pmatrix}$ **7.** $\begin{pmatrix} 1.36 & 0.48 \\ 0.48 & 1.64 \end{pmatrix}$ **8.** $\begin{pmatrix} \frac{1}{2} & \frac{1}{4} \\ 1 & \frac{1}{2} \end{pmatrix}$

In Questions 9 – 12, find all the invariant lines for the transformations with the given matrices.

9. $\begin{pmatrix} -1 & 2 \\ -2 & 3 \end{pmatrix}$ **10.** $\begin{pmatrix} 10 & 3 \\ 3 & 2 \end{pmatrix}$ **11.** $\begin{pmatrix} 2 & -1 \\ -1 & 2 \end{pmatrix}$ **12.** $\begin{pmatrix} 3\frac{1}{2} & -\frac{1}{2} \\ -\frac{1}{2} & 3\frac{1}{2} \end{pmatrix}$

13. The matrix $\mathbf{M} = \begin{pmatrix} 4 & 3 \\ 9 & 10 \end{pmatrix}$ transforms the point (x, y) to (x', y'), where

$$\begin{pmatrix} x' \\ y' \end{pmatrix} = \begin{pmatrix} 4 & 3 \\ 9 & 10 \end{pmatrix}\begin{pmatrix} x \\ y \end{pmatrix}$$

(i) By considering the image of $(1, m)$ under the transformation given by **M**, or otherwise, find the two values of m for which $y = mx$ is an invariant line of the transformation.

(ii) Draw a sketch showing these two invariant lines, and for both values of m indicate how the point $(1, m)$ is transformed by **M**.

(iii) Show that $y = 3x + 4$ is also an invariant line under this transformation.

[MEI 1993]

14. The transformation T maps $\begin{pmatrix} x \\ y \end{pmatrix}$ to $\begin{pmatrix} a & c \\ b & d \end{pmatrix}\begin{pmatrix} x \\ y \end{pmatrix}$, where a, b, c, d are not all 0. Show that all lines through the origin are invariant under T if and only if $b = c = 0$ and $a = d \neq 0$.

15. The point P (x, y) is mapped into the point P′(x', y') by the transformation

$$\begin{pmatrix} x' \\ y' \end{pmatrix} = \mathbf{A}\begin{pmatrix} x \\ y \end{pmatrix} \text{ where } \mathbf{A} = \begin{pmatrix} 1 & -1 \\ 3 & -3 \end{pmatrix}$$

(i) What is the value of the determinant of the matrix **A**?

(ii) The point Q $(1, m)$ is transformed into the point Q′(k, km). Find the values of k and m. Hence give the equations of the invariant lines of the transformation.

Exercise 4G continued

  (iii) Draw a sketch and describe the transformation of the plane represented by **A** with reference to the points on the lines $y = x, y = x + 1, y = x - 2$.

  (iv) Which points transform to the point $(3, 9)$?

[MEI 1992]

16. (i) M is a reflection of the plane such that the point (x', y') is the image of the point (x, y) where

$$\begin{pmatrix} x' \\ y' \end{pmatrix} = \begin{pmatrix} -0.6 & 0.8 \\ 0.8 & 0.6 \end{pmatrix} \begin{pmatrix} x \\ y \end{pmatrix}$$

Find a point, other than the origin, that is invariant under this reflection. Hence find the equation of the mirror line.

   (ii) T is a translation of the plane by the vector $\begin{pmatrix} a \\ b \end{pmatrix}$. The point (X, Y) is the image of the point (x, y) under the combined transformation TM (that is M followed by T), where

$$\begin{pmatrix} X \\ Y \\ 1 \end{pmatrix} = \begin{pmatrix} -0.6 & 0.8 & a \\ 0.8 & 0.6 & b \\ 0 & 0 & 1 \end{pmatrix} \begin{pmatrix} x \\ y \\ 1 \end{pmatrix}$$

   (a) Show that if $a = -4$ and $b = 2$ then $(0, 5)$ is an invariant point of TM.

   (b) Show that if $a = 2$ and $b = 1$ then TM has no invariant point.

   (c) Find a relation between a and b that must be satisfied if TM is to have any invariant points.

[SMP 1993]

Investigations

1. Investigate the sequence of matrices $\mathbf{I}, \mathbf{M}, \mathbf{M}^2, \mathbf{M}^3, \ldots$ where $\mathbf{M} = \begin{pmatrix} 1 & 1 \\ 1 & 0 \end{pmatrix}$.

2. Mendel's genetic theory states that offspring inherit characteristics from their parents through their genes. Each characteristic is controlled by a pair of genes, which may be of two types: G or g. The three possible combinations are

  GG   known as homozygous dominant, and denoted by H

  Gg or gG   known as heterozygous, and denoted by H

  gg   known as homozygous recessive, and denoted by R

Offspring inherit one gene from each parent, randomly and independently. In a controlled study of a population of fruit flies, the only females allowed to mate are those known to be heterozygous.

Investigations continued

(i) The unfinished table shows the probability that the offspring has combination D, H or R given the combination of genes of the male parent. Complete the table to construct the matrix **M** containing this information.

Male parent

$$\text{Offspring} \begin{array}{c} \\ D \\ H \\ R \end{array} \begin{array}{ccc} D & H & R \\ \left(\begin{array}{ccc} \frac{1}{2} & \frac{1}{4} & 0 \\ \dots & \dots & \dots \\ \dots & \dots & \dots \end{array} \right) \end{array}$$

(ii) Initially the proportions of D, H and R combinations in the population are given by $x_0 = \begin{pmatrix} d \\ h \\ r \end{pmatrix}$. Show that $x_1 = Mx_0$ gives the proportions in the next generation.

(iii) Investigate what happens if the study continues over many generations.

3. The transformation S is represented by the matrix $\begin{pmatrix} 2 & -3 \\ 3 & 2 \end{pmatrix}$; transformation T maps the point Z on the Argand diagram (representing the complex number z) to the point which represents $z(2 + 3j)$. Compare the effects of S and T, and investigate further.

- The matrix $\mathbf{M} = \begin{pmatrix} a & c \\ b & d \end{pmatrix}$ represents the transformation which maps

  the point with position vector $\begin{pmatrix} x \\ y \end{pmatrix}$ to the point with position

  vector $\begin{pmatrix} x' \\ y' \end{pmatrix}$, where $\begin{cases} x' = ax + cy \\ y' = bx + dy \end{cases}$.

- The image of $\begin{pmatrix} 1 \\ 0 \end{pmatrix}$ is the first column of $\mathbf{M}$; the image of $\begin{pmatrix} 0 \\ 1 \end{pmatrix}$ is

  the second column of $\mathbf{M}$.

- Matrix multiplication

  Row from left matrix with column from right matrix

$$\begin{pmatrix} p & r \\ q & s \end{pmatrix} \begin{pmatrix} a & c \\ b & d \end{pmatrix} = \begin{pmatrix} pa + rb & pc + rd \\ qa + sb & qc + sd \end{pmatrix}$$

- Matrix multiplication is associative: $\mathbf{N(ML)} = \mathbf{(NM)L}$.

- The *determinant* of the matrix $\mathbf{M} = \begin{pmatrix} a & c \\ b & d \end{pmatrix}$ is $ad - bc$. It is denoted

  by $|\mathbf{M}|$, det $\mathbf{M}$, or $\begin{vmatrix} a & c \\ b & d \end{vmatrix}$.

- The inverse of $\mathbf{M} = \begin{pmatrix} a & c \\ b & d \end{pmatrix}$ is $\mathbf{M}^{-1} = \dfrac{1}{ad - bc} \begin{pmatrix} d & -c \\ -b & a \end{pmatrix}$, provided

  $|ad - bc| \neq 0$.

- Note the order for the inverse of a product: $(\mathbf{AB})^{-1} = \mathbf{B}^{-1}\mathbf{A}^{-1}$.

- If transformation T is such that $T(\lambda \mathbf{p} + \mu \mathbf{q}) = \lambda T(\mathbf{p}) + \mu T(\mathbf{q})$,
  whatever the scalars λ and μ, and whatever the vectors $\mathbf{p}$ and $\mathbf{q}$,
  then T is known as a *linear transformation*.

- When solving n simultaneous equations in n unknowns: there is
  a unique solution if det $\mathbf{M} \neq 0$; if det $\mathbf{M} = 0$ we have either no
  solutions or infinitely many solutions.

- The line AB is known as an *invariant line* under T if the image of
  each point on AB is on AB.

Matrices

4

5

Vector geometry

I pulled out, on the spot, a pocket book, which still exists, and made an entry, on which, at the very moment, I felt it might be worth my while to expend the labour of at least ten (or it might be fifteen) years to come. But then it is fair to say that this was because I felt a problem to have been at that moment solved, an intellectual want relieved, which had haunted me for at least fifteen years before.

William R Hamilton, writing on 16 October 1858 about his invention of quaternions on 16 October 1843

Multiplying vectors: the scalar product

In Pure Mathematics 3 you met the scalar product $\mathbf{a.b}$ of two vectors, $\mathbf{a}$ and $\mathbf{b}$:

$$\mathbf{a.b} = |\mathbf{a}|\,|\mathbf{b}|\cos\theta$$

where θ is the angle between $\mathbf{a}$ and $\mathbf{b}$, the result being a scalar (figure 5.1).

Figure 5.1

In two dimensions: $\mathbf{a} = \begin{pmatrix} a_1 \\ a_2 \end{pmatrix}$ $\mathbf{b} = \begin{pmatrix} b_1 \\ b_2 \end{pmatrix}$ $\Rightarrow$ $\mathbf{a.b} = a_1 b_1 + a_2 b_2$

In three dimensions: $\mathbf{a} = \begin{pmatrix} a_1 \\ a_2 \\ a_3 \end{pmatrix}$ $\mathbf{b} = \begin{pmatrix} b_1 \\ b_2 \\ b_3 \end{pmatrix}$ $\Rightarrow$ $\mathbf{a.b} = a_1 b_1 + a_2 b_2 + a_3 b_3$

Using the scalar product is an efficient way of finding the angle between two vectors. It is particularly convenient if you want to test whether two vectors are perpendicular, as then the scalar product is zero.

The scalar product also enables us to write down the equation of a plane: the equation of a plane is $\mathbf{n.(r - a)} = 0$, where $\mathbf{a}$ is the position vector of the point A on the plane, $\mathbf{r}$ is the position vector of a general point on the plane, and $\mathbf{n}$ is a 'normal', a vector perpendicular to the plane (see figure 5.2). This equation can be re-arranged as $\mathbf{n.r} = \mathbf{n.a}$, a scalar constant.

Figure 5.2

If $\mathbf{n} = \begin{pmatrix} n_1 \\ n_2 \\ n_3 \end{pmatrix}$ and $\mathbf{r} = \begin{pmatrix} x \\ y \\ z \end{pmatrix}$ the equation can be further re-arranged as

$n_1 x + n_2 y + n_3 z + d = 0$, where d is a constant. (This is known as the Cartesian form.)

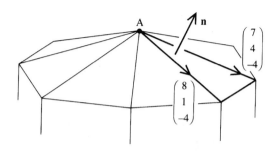

Figure 5.3

Suppose, for example, an architect is designing a new roof with several triangular sections (figure 5.3). He decides he needs to find the Cartesian equation of the plane containing the triangle with vertex A (3, 2, 10) and

sloping edges given by the vectors $\begin{pmatrix} 8 \\ 1 \\ -4 \end{pmatrix}$ and $\begin{pmatrix} 7 \\ 4 \\ -4 \end{pmatrix}$. If he could easily find

a normal $\mathbf{n}$ for the plane, finding the equation of the plane would only

involve evaluating $\mathbf{n.a}$. The normal $\mathbf{n}$ is perpendicular to both $\begin{pmatrix} 8 \\ 1 \\ -4 \end{pmatrix}$ and $\begin{pmatrix} 7 \\ 4 \\ -4 \end{pmatrix}$

so the problem reduces to one of finding a vector perpendicular to two given vectors. One such vector is the vector product, which we now introduce.

Multiplying vectors: the vector product

The *vector product* of **a** and **b** is a vector perpendicular to both **a** and **b**; its magnitude is |**a**||**b**| sinθ, where θ is the angle between **a** and **b**. The vector product of **a** and **b** is written as **a** $\times$ **b**. Thus

$$\mathbf{a} \times \mathbf{b} = |\mathbf{a}||\mathbf{b}| \sin \theta \,\hat{\mathbf{n}}$$

where θ is the angle between **a** and **b**, and $\hat{\mathbf{n}}$ is a unit vector which is perpendicular to both **a** and **b**.

There are two unit vectors perpendicular to both **a** and **b**, but they point in opposite directions; we sometimes say they have opposite *senses*. Our vector $\hat{\mathbf{n}}$ is chosen such that **a**, **b** and $\hat{\mathbf{n}}$ (in that order) form a right-handed set of vectors: if **a** and **b** are both horizontal, and if an anticlockwise rotation (between 0° and 180°) is needed to turn **a** to point in the same direction as **b**, then **a** $\times$ **b** is the upwards vertical, as illustrated in figure 5.4. If you point the thumb of your right hand in the direction of **a**, and your index finger in the direction of **b**, then your second finger coming 'up' from your palm, points in the direction of **a** $\times$ **b**.

Figure 5.4

The following are among the important properties of vector products.

1. The vector product is anti-commutative

The vector products **a** $\times$ **b** and **b** $\times$ **a** have the same magnitude but are in opposite directions, so that **a** $\times$ **b** = –**b** $\times$ **a**. This is known as the *anti-commutative property*.

2. The vector product of parallel vectors is 0

This is because the angle θ between two parallel vectors is 0° or 180°, so that sin θ = 0. Thus **a** $\times$ **a** = **0** and in particular **i** $\times$ **i** = **0**.

Notice that **a** $\times$ **b** is also **0** if **a** or **b** is **0**.

3. Multiplication by scalars

If m is a scalar, the vector $m\mathbf{a}$ has magnitude $|m||\mathbf{a}|$; $m\mathbf{a}$ and $\mathbf{a}$ have the same direction if m is positive, but opposite directions if m is negative. Similar comments apply to $n\mathbf{b}$ and $\mathbf{b}$. Whatever the signs of m and n,

$$(m\mathbf{a}) \times (n\mathbf{b}) = mn(\mathbf{a} \times \mathbf{b})$$

4. The distributive property of vector product over vector addition

The property that $p(q + r) = pq + pr$, whatever the values of the numbers p, q and r, is known as the distributive property of multiplication over addition. It enables you to change a product into a sum of two simpler products – in doing so the multiplication is 'distributed' over the two terms of the original sum. Similarly, the process of forming a vector product is distributive over vector addition:

$$\mathbf{a} \times (\mathbf{b} + \mathbf{c}) = \mathbf{a} \times \mathbf{b} + \mathbf{a} \times \mathbf{c}$$

This is clearly true for the trivial case of $\mathbf{a} = \mathbf{0}$, as then both sides simplify to $\mathbf{0}$, but we postpone the general proof to page 156. The alternative form of the distributive property also holds, for

$$\mathbf{a} \times (\mathbf{b} + \mathbf{c}) = \mathbf{a} \times \mathbf{b} + \mathbf{a} \times \mathbf{c}$$

$$\Rightarrow \quad -\mathbf{a} \times (\mathbf{b} + \mathbf{c}) = -\mathbf{a} \times \mathbf{b} - \mathbf{a} \times \mathbf{c}$$

$$\Rightarrow \quad (\mathbf{b} + \mathbf{c}) \times \mathbf{a} = \mathbf{b} \times \mathbf{a} + \mathbf{c} \times \mathbf{a}$$

> Multiplying by –1

> By the anti-commutative property

5. The vector product in component form

We shall shortly prove that if we express vectors $\mathbf{a}$ and $\mathbf{b}$ in terms of their components, so that $\mathbf{a} = a_1\mathbf{i} + a_2\mathbf{j} + a_3\mathbf{k}$ and $\mathbf{b} = b_1\mathbf{i} + b_2\mathbf{j} + b_3\mathbf{k}$, then

$$\mathbf{a} \times \mathbf{b} = \begin{pmatrix} a_1 \\ a_2 \\ a_3 \end{pmatrix} \times \begin{pmatrix} b_1 \\ b_2 \\ b_3 \end{pmatrix} = \begin{pmatrix} a_2b_3 - a_3b_2 \\ a_3b_1 - a_1b_3 \\ a_1b_2 - a_2b_1 \end{pmatrix}$$

Activity

In this activity you may find it helpful to take the near edge of a rectangular table as the x axis, the left edge of the table as the y axis, and to hold a ruler pointing vertically upwards to represent the positive z axis, as in the diagram.

Use pens to represent: **i**, the unit vector pointing to the right along the x axis;

j, the unit vector pointing away from you along the y axis;

k, the unit vector pointing up along the z axis.

The vector product of **a** and **b** is defined as $\mathbf{a} \times \mathbf{b} = |\mathbf{a}||\mathbf{b}| \sin \theta \, \hat{\mathbf{n}}$, where θ is the angle between **a** and **b**, and $\hat{\mathbf{n}}$ is a unit vector which is perpendicular to both **a** and **b**, such that **a**, **b** and $\hat{\mathbf{n}}$ (in that order) form a right-handed set of vectors.

Using the definition, check the truth of each of the following nine results:

$$\mathbf{i} \times \mathbf{i} = 0 \qquad \mathbf{i} \times \mathbf{j} = \mathbf{k} \qquad \mathbf{i} \times \mathbf{k} = -\mathbf{j}$$

$$\mathbf{j} \times \mathbf{i} = -\mathbf{k} \qquad \mathbf{j} \times \mathbf{j} = 0 \qquad \mathbf{j} \times \mathbf{k} = \mathbf{i}$$

$$\mathbf{k} \times \mathbf{i} = \mathbf{j} \qquad \mathbf{k} \times \mathbf{j} = -\mathbf{i} \qquad \mathbf{k} \times \mathbf{k} = 0$$

(This is the first place in your work with vectors where it has been important that the positive x, y, z axes form a right-handed set.)

If $\mathbf{a} = a_1\mathbf{i} + a_2\mathbf{j} + a_3\mathbf{k}$ and $\mathbf{b} = b_1\mathbf{i} + b_2\mathbf{j} + b_3\mathbf{k}$, then

$$\mathbf{a} \times \mathbf{b} = (a_1\mathbf{i} + a_2\mathbf{j} + a_3\mathbf{k}) \times (b_1\mathbf{i} + b_2\mathbf{j} + b_3\mathbf{k})$$

Using properties 3 and 4 several times

$$= a_1b_1\mathbf{i} \times \mathbf{i} + a_1b_2\mathbf{i} \times \mathbf{j} + a_1b_3\mathbf{i} \times \mathbf{k}$$
$$+ a_2b_1\mathbf{j} \times \mathbf{i} + a_2b_2\mathbf{j} \times \mathbf{j} + a_2b_3\mathbf{j} \times \mathbf{k}$$
$$+ a_3b_1\mathbf{k} \times \mathbf{i} + a_3b_2\mathbf{k} \times \mathbf{j} + a_3b_3\mathbf{k} \times \mathbf{k}$$

Since $\mathbf{i} \times \mathbf{i} = 0$, $\mathbf{i} \times \mathbf{j} = \mathbf{k}$, $\mathbf{i} \times \mathbf{k} = -\mathbf{j}$, etc.

$$= 0 + a_1b_2\mathbf{k} - a_1b_3\mathbf{j} - a_2b_1\mathbf{k} + 0 + a_2b_3\mathbf{i} + a_3b_1\mathbf{j} - a_3b_2\mathbf{i} + 0$$

$$= (a_2b_3 - a_3b_2)\mathbf{i} + (a_3b_1 - a_1b_3)\mathbf{j} + (a_1b_2 - a_2b_1)\mathbf{k}$$

Thus

$$\mathbf{a} \times \mathbf{b} = \begin{pmatrix} a_1 \\ a_2 \\ a_3 \end{pmatrix} \times \begin{pmatrix} b_1 \\ b_2 \\ b_3 \end{pmatrix} = \begin{pmatrix} a_2b_3 - a_3b_2 \\ a_3b_1 - a_1b_3 \\ a_1b_2 - a_2b_1 \end{pmatrix}$$

The first component of $\mathbf{a} \times \mathbf{b}$ is the value of the 2×2 determinant $\begin{vmatrix} a_2 & b_2 \\ a_3 & b_3 \end{vmatrix}$

obtained by covering up the top row of $\begin{pmatrix} a_1 \\ a_2 \\ a_3 \end{pmatrix} \times \begin{pmatrix} b_1 \\ b_2 \\ b_3 \end{pmatrix}$; the second component

is the negative of the 2×2 determinant obtained by covering up the middle row (note the sign); and the third component is the 2×2 determinant obtained by covering up the bottom row. We may therefore write

$$\mathbf{a} \times \mathbf{b} = \begin{pmatrix} a_1 \\ a_2 \\ a_3 \end{pmatrix} \times \begin{pmatrix} b_1 \\ b_2 \\ b_3 \end{pmatrix} = \begin{vmatrix} a_2 & b_2 \\ a_3 & b_3 \end{vmatrix} \mathbf{i} - \begin{vmatrix} a_1 & b_1 \\ a_3 & b_3 \end{vmatrix} \mathbf{j} + \begin{vmatrix} a_1 & b_1 \\ a_2 & b_2 \end{vmatrix} \mathbf{k}$$

Note this sign

EXAMPLE

Calculate $\mathbf{a} \times \mathbf{b}$ when $\mathbf{a} = 3\mathbf{i} + 2\mathbf{j} + 5\mathbf{k}$ and $\mathbf{b} = \mathbf{i} - 4\mathbf{j} + 2\mathbf{k}$.

Solution 1

$$\mathbf{a} \times \mathbf{b} = \begin{pmatrix} 3 \\ 2 \\ 5 \end{pmatrix} \times \begin{pmatrix} 1 \\ -4 \\ 2 \end{pmatrix} = \begin{pmatrix} 2 \times 2 - 5 \times (-4) \\ 5 \times 1 - 3 \times 2 \\ 3 \times (-4) - 2 \times 1 \end{pmatrix} = \begin{pmatrix} 24 \\ -1 \\ -14 \end{pmatrix}$$

Solution 2

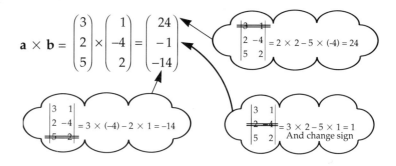

$$\mathbf{a} \times \mathbf{b} = \begin{pmatrix} 3 \\ 2 \\ 5 \end{pmatrix} \times \begin{pmatrix} 1 \\ -4 \\ 2 \end{pmatrix} = \begin{pmatrix} 24 \\ -1 \\ -14 \end{pmatrix}$$

$\begin{vmatrix} 2 & -4 \\ 5 & 2 \end{vmatrix} = 2 \times 2 - 5 \times (-4) = 24$

$\begin{vmatrix} 3 & 1 \\ 2 & -4 \end{vmatrix} = 3 \times (-4) - 2 \times 1 = -14$

$\begin{vmatrix} 3 & 1 \\ 2 & -4 \\ 5 & 2 \end{vmatrix} = 3 \times 2 - 5 \times 1 = 1$ And change sign

EXAMPLE

Find $\mathbf{n} = \begin{pmatrix} 8 \\ 1 \\ -4 \end{pmatrix} \times \begin{pmatrix} 7 \\ 4 \\ -4 \end{pmatrix}$ and hence find the equation of the plane which

contains the point A(3, 2, 10) and the vectors $\begin{pmatrix} 8 \\ 1 \\ -4 \end{pmatrix}$ and $\begin{pmatrix} 7 \\ 4 \\ -4 \end{pmatrix}$.

(This is the architect's problem posed on page 135).

Solution

$$\mathbf{n} = \begin{pmatrix} 8 \\ 1 \\ -4 \end{pmatrix} \times \begin{pmatrix} 7 \\ 4 \\ -4 \end{pmatrix} = \begin{pmatrix} 1 \times (-4) - (-4) \times 4 \\ -(8 \times (-4) - (-4) \times 7) \\ 8 \times 4 - 1 \times 7 \end{pmatrix} = \begin{pmatrix} 12 \\ 4 \\ 25 \end{pmatrix}$$

The Cartesian equation of the plane is $12x + 4y + 25z = $ constant. As (3, 2, 10) is on the plane, the constant is $12 \times 3 + 4 \times 2 + 25 \times 10 = 294$. The equation of the plane is $12x + 4y + 25z = 294$.

Activity

Some calculators can handle vectors. If yours does, or if you have access to a computer algebra system that handles vectors, find out how to use it to calculate the vector product of two vectors.

If you are going to use your vector product for further calculation it is wise to check that your result is perpendicular to both $\mathbf{a}$ and $\mathbf{b}$. This can be done by checking (perhaps mentally) that the scalar product of your result with both $\mathbf{a}$ and $\mathbf{b}$ is indeed zero.

For Discussion

Is it not possible to find the vector product of two two-dimensional vectors?

EXAMPLE Find the Cartesian equation of the plane which contains the points A(3, 4, 2), B(2, 0, 5), C(6, 7, 8).

Solution

We need to find a vector which is perpendicular to AB and BC (and CA).

$$\overrightarrow{AB} = \begin{pmatrix} 2 \\ 0 \\ 5 \end{pmatrix} - \begin{pmatrix} 3 \\ 4 \\ 2 \end{pmatrix} = \begin{pmatrix} -1 \\ -4 \\ 3 \end{pmatrix} \qquad \overrightarrow{BC} = \begin{pmatrix} 6 \\ 7 \\ 8 \end{pmatrix} - \begin{pmatrix} 2 \\ 0 \\ 5 \end{pmatrix} = \begin{pmatrix} 4 \\ 7 \\ 3 \end{pmatrix}$$

$$\Rightarrow \overrightarrow{AB} \times \overrightarrow{BC} = \begin{pmatrix} -1 \\ -4 \\ 3 \end{pmatrix} \times \begin{pmatrix} 4 \\ 7 \\ 3 \end{pmatrix} = \begin{pmatrix} -33 \\ 15 \\ 9 \end{pmatrix} = -3 \begin{pmatrix} 11 \\ -5 \\ -3 \end{pmatrix}$$

so $\mathbf{n} = \begin{pmatrix} 11 \\ -5 \\ -3 \end{pmatrix}$ is a vector perpendicular to plane ABC.

> Mentally check that $\mathbf{n}.\overrightarrow{AB} = \mathbf{n}.\overrightarrow{BC} = 0$

Plane ABC has equation $11x - 5y - 3z = $ constant. We can find the value of the constant by substituting the co-ordinates of A or B or C, obtaining 7. The Cartesian equation of plane ABC is $11x - 5y - 3z = 7$.

Note how it was helpful to remove common factors from the components of $\overrightarrow{AB} \times \overrightarrow{BC}$ so as to produce the simplest possible equation.

Finally here is an example where we are not expressing the vectors in terms of their components.

> Distributive property applied twice. Notice the importance of keeping factors in their correct order

EXAMPLE Simplify: $(\mathbf{a} - \mathbf{b}) \times (\mathbf{a} + \mathbf{b})$.

Solution

$(\mathbf{a} - \mathbf{b}) \times (\mathbf{a} + \mathbf{b}) = \mathbf{a} \times \mathbf{a} + \mathbf{a} \times \mathbf{b} - \mathbf{b} \times \mathbf{a} - \mathbf{b} \times \mathbf{b}$

$\qquad = 0 + \mathbf{a} \times \mathbf{b} - \mathbf{b} \times \mathbf{a} - 0$

> Vector product of parallel vectors is **0**

$\qquad = \mathbf{a} \times \mathbf{b} + \mathbf{a} \times \mathbf{b}$

> Anti-commutative property

$\qquad = 2\mathbf{a} \times \mathbf{b}$

**HISTORICAL
NOTE**
*The Irish mathematician William Rowan Hamilton (1805–1865) was appointed
Professor of Astronomy at Trinity College, Dublin, at the age of 21, a post he held
till the year of his death. Hamilton set out to create an algebra which was related to
the rotation of three-dimensional space in much the same way that the algebra of
complex numbers is related to the rotation of the plane. He defined a 'quaternion'
as the sum of a real number and a 'triplet', a triplet being what we call a vector.
For many years he was hampered because he expected to preserve the commutative
property of multiplication; this turned out to be impossible in an algebra of three-
dimensional rotations, and he finally defined multiplication in such a way that
$\mathbf{a} \times \mathbf{b} = -\mathbf{b} \times \mathbf{a}$, though it appears that Carl Friedrich Gauss (1777–1855) had
reached similar results about 30 years previously. Also in Germany, Hermann
Günther Grassmann (1809–1877) independently developed similar ideas.
Quaternions did not long survive Hamilton, but vectors became a major tool for
physicists, though not all considered them useful. Even the eminent Lord Kelvin
(1824–1907) wrote: 'Vector is a useless survival or off-shoot from quaternion and
has never been of the slightest use to any creature.'*

Exercise 5A

1. Calculate each of the following vector products.

(a) $\begin{pmatrix} 3 \\ 5 \\ 2 \end{pmatrix} \times \begin{pmatrix} 2 \\ 4 \\ -3 \end{pmatrix}$ (b) $\begin{pmatrix} 7 \\ -4 \\ -5 \end{pmatrix} \times \begin{pmatrix} -4 \\ 5 \\ -3 \end{pmatrix}$

(c) $\begin{pmatrix} 5 \\ -2 \\ 4 \end{pmatrix} \times \begin{pmatrix} 1 \\ 5 \\ -6 \end{pmatrix}$ (d) $(3\mathbf{i} - 7\mathbf{k}) \times (2\mathbf{i} + 3\mathbf{j} + 5\mathbf{k})$

2. The distributive property of vector product over vector addition
states that

$\mathbf{a} \times (\mathbf{b} + \mathbf{c}) = \mathbf{a} \times \mathbf{b} + \mathbf{a} \times \mathbf{c}$ and $(\mathbf{a} + \mathbf{b}) \times \mathbf{c} = \mathbf{a} \times \mathbf{c} + \mathbf{b} \times \mathbf{c}$.

Check that these are both true when

$\mathbf{a} = 3\mathbf{i} + 4\mathbf{j} + 6\mathbf{k}$ $\mathbf{b} = 8\mathbf{i} + 2\mathbf{j} + 5\mathbf{k}$ $\mathbf{c} = 7\mathbf{i} - 3\mathbf{j} + 9\mathbf{k}$

3. Find vectors perpendicular to the following pairs of vectors:

(a) $\begin{pmatrix} 2 \\ 0 \\ 5 \end{pmatrix}, \begin{pmatrix} 3 \\ -1 \\ -2 \end{pmatrix}$ (b) $\begin{pmatrix} 12 \\ 3 \\ -2 \end{pmatrix}, \begin{pmatrix} 7 \\ 1 \\ 4 \end{pmatrix}$ (c) $\begin{pmatrix} 2 \\ 3 \\ 4 \end{pmatrix}, \begin{pmatrix} 3 \\ 6 \\ 7 \end{pmatrix}$ (d) $\begin{pmatrix} 3 \\ -4 \\ 6 \end{pmatrix}, \begin{pmatrix} 8 \\ 5 \\ -3 \end{pmatrix}$

4. Find a unit vector perpendicular to both $\mathbf{i} + 2\mathbf{j} + 7\mathbf{k}$ and $3\mathbf{i} - \mathbf{j} + 6\mathbf{k}$.

5. Find the Cartesian equations of the planes containing the three points

(a) M(1, 4, 2), E(5, 1, 3), I(1, 0, 0)   (b) T(5, –3, 4), J(0, 1, 0), H(6, 2, 5)

(c) D(6, 2, –2), R(1, 4, 3), M(–5, 7, 1)   (d) C(4, 2, –1), L(8, 2, 4), S(5, 8, –7)

Exercise 5A continued

6. The angle between $\mathbf{p} = \begin{pmatrix} 5 \\ -3 \\ 1 \end{pmatrix}$ and $\mathbf{q} = \begin{pmatrix} -2 \\ -5 \\ 2 \end{pmatrix}$ is θ.

(i) Calculate $\mathbf{p} \times \mathbf{q}$ and $|\mathbf{p} \times \mathbf{q}|$ and hence find the value of $\sin\theta$.

(ii) Calculate $\mathbf{p.q}$ and hence find the value of $\cos\theta$.

(iii) Show that the results you obtained in (i) and (ii) fit the identity

$$\sin^2\theta + \cos^2\theta \equiv 1$$

(iv) If you want to find the angle between two vectors it is usually quicker to use the scalar product rather than the vector product. Give another reason why the scalar product method is preferable.

7. What can you say about a and b if $\mathbf{a} \times \mathbf{c} = \mathbf{b} \times \mathbf{c}$?

8. Explain why $\mathbf{a.(a} \times \mathbf{b}) = 0$.

9. In triangle ABC, let $\overrightarrow{BC}$, $\overrightarrow{CA}$, and $\overrightarrow{AB}$ be denoted by **a**, **b**, and **c**, as illustrated. Show that $\mathbf{a} \times \mathbf{b} = \mathbf{b} \times \mathbf{c} = \mathbf{c} \times \mathbf{a}$, and use this result to complete an alternative proof of the Sine Rule.

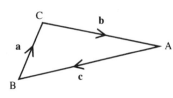

10. The moment of force **F** about the origin O is $\mathbf{r} \times \mathbf{F}$, where **r** is the position vector of any point R on the line of action of **F** . Prove that the moment of a force about O is independent of the choice of the point R, provided R is on the line of action of **F**.

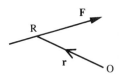

11. If a body is rotating at angular speed ω about an axis through O (see diagram) then we represent the angular velocity by the vector ω, defined to have magnitude ω and be parallel to the axis such that a right-handed corkscrew attached to the body would move in the direction indicated by ω.

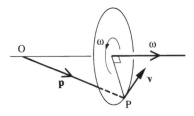

Show that the velocity **v** of a point P on the rotating body is given by $\mathbf{v} = \omega \times \mathbf{p}$, where **p** is the position vector of P.

The intersection of two planes

If you look around you will find objects which can be used to represent planes – walls, floors, ceilings, doors, roofs, and so on. You will see that the intersection of two planes is a straight line.

EXAMPLE

Find ℓ, the line of intersection of the two planes

$$3x + 2y - 3z = -18 \quad \text{and} \quad x - 2y + z = 12$$

Solution 1

This solution depends on finding two points on ℓ.

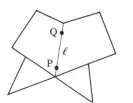

We can find one point by arbitrarily choosing to put $y = 0$ into the equations of the planes and solving simultaneously:

$$\left. \begin{matrix} 3x - 3z = -18 \\ x + y = 12 \end{matrix} \right\} \Leftrightarrow \left\{ \begin{matrix} x - z = -6 \\ x + z = 12 \end{matrix} \right\} \Leftrightarrow x = 3, z = 9$$

So P with co-ordinates $(3, 0, 9)$ is a point on ℓ.

(We could run into difficulties putting $y = 0$ as it is possible that the line has no points where $y = 0$. In this case our simultaneous equations for x and z would be inconsistent; we would then choose a value for x or z instead.)

Choosing to put $z = 1$ into the equations gives

$$\left. \begin{matrix} 3x + 2y = -15 \\ x - 2y = 11 \end{matrix} \right\} \Leftrightarrow \left\{ \begin{matrix} 4x = -4 \\ 2y = x - 11 \end{matrix} \right\} \Leftrightarrow x = -1, y = -6.$$

so Q with co-ordinates $(-1, -6, 1)$ is a point on ℓ.

$$\overrightarrow{PQ} = \begin{pmatrix} -1 \\ -6 \\ 1 \end{pmatrix} - \begin{pmatrix} 3 \\ 0 \\ 9 \end{pmatrix} = \begin{pmatrix} -4 \\ -6 \\ -8 \end{pmatrix} = -2 \begin{pmatrix} 2 \\ 3 \\ 4 \end{pmatrix}$$

> Removing factor -2 makes the arithmetic simpler

so we use $\begin{pmatrix} 2 \\ 3 \\ 4 \end{pmatrix}$ as the direction vector for ℓ.

A vector equation for ℓ is $\mathbf{r} = \begin{pmatrix} -1 \\ -6 \\ 1 \end{pmatrix} + t \begin{pmatrix} 2 \\ 3 \\ 4 \end{pmatrix}$.

We may give the Cartesian form of the equations: $\dfrac{x+1}{2} = \dfrac{y+6}{3} = \dfrac{z-1}{4}$

or the parametric form: $\begin{cases} x = 2t - 1 \\ y = 3t - 6 \\ z = 4t + 1 \end{cases}$

Solution 2

The planes have normals $\mathbf{n}_1 = \begin{pmatrix} 3 \\ 2 \\ -3 \end{pmatrix}$ and $\mathbf{n}_2 = \begin{pmatrix} 1 \\ -2 \\ 1 \end{pmatrix}$.

As line ℓ is in each plane (see figure) it must be perpendicular to both $\mathbf{n}_1$ and $\mathbf{n}_2$, so

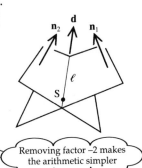

$$\mathbf{n}_1 \times \mathbf{n}_2 = \begin{pmatrix} -4 \\ -6 \\ -8 \end{pmatrix} = -2\begin{pmatrix} 2 \\ 3 \\ 4 \end{pmatrix}$$

gives us a vector in the direction of ℓ.

Removing factor −2 makes the arithmetic simpler

We shall use $\mathbf{d} = \begin{pmatrix} 2 \\ 3 \\ 4 \end{pmatrix}$ as the direction vector for ℓ.

Mentally check that $\mathbf{d}.\mathbf{n}_1 = \mathbf{d}.\mathbf{n}_2 = 0$

Now we only need to find a point S on ℓ.

Choosing to put $x = 1$ into the equations gives

$$\begin{rcases} 2y - 3z = -21 \\ -2y + z = 11 \end{rcases} \Leftrightarrow \begin{rcases} -2z = -10 \\ 2y = 3z - 21 \end{rcases} \Leftrightarrow z = 5,\ y = -3$$

so S with co-ordinates $(1, -3, 5)$ is a point on line ℓ.

The Cartesian equations of ℓ are $\dfrac{x-1}{2} = \dfrac{y+3}{3} = \dfrac{z-5}{4}$, though we could give

the parametric form $\begin{cases} x = 2t + 1 \\ y = 3t - 3 \\ z = 4t + 5 \end{cases}$ or the vector form $\mathbf{r} = \begin{pmatrix} 1 \\ -3 \\ 5 \end{pmatrix} + t\begin{pmatrix} 2 \\ 3 \\ 4 \end{pmatrix}$.

NOTE

These equations do not look the same as our previous equations because we have used S $(1, -3, 5)$ instead of Q $(-1, -6, 1)$ as our 'starting point' for the line. There are infinitely many 'starting points' available. Putting $x = -1$ in the equations obtained at the end of Solution 2 gives $t = -1$, $y = -6$, $z = 1$, showing that the line does go through the point Q $(-1, -6, 1)$: our two solutions are equivalent as they have a common point and the same direction vector.

Solution 3

In this solution we solve the original two equations in x, y and z, expressing each of x, y and z in terms of some parameter.

Put $x = \lambda$ into $\begin{cases} 3x + 2y - 3z = -18 \\ x - 2y + z = 12 \end{cases}$ and solve simultaneously for y and z:

$$\left.\begin{array}{l} 2y - 3z = -18 - 3\lambda \\ -2y + z = 12 - \lambda \end{array}\right\} \quad \Rightarrow \quad -2z = -6 - 4\lambda \quad \Rightarrow \quad z = 2\lambda + 3$$

so that $2y = 3z - 18 - 3\lambda = 3(2\lambda + 3) - 18 - 3\lambda = 3\lambda - 9$ and $y = \frac{3}{2}\lambda - \frac{9}{2}$.

Thus the parametric equations for ℓ are

$$\begin{array}{c} x = \lambda \\ y = \frac{3}{2}\lambda - \frac{9}{2} \quad \text{or} \quad \begin{pmatrix} x \\ y \\ z \end{pmatrix} = \begin{pmatrix} 0 \\ -\frac{9}{2} \\ 3 \end{pmatrix} + \lambda \begin{pmatrix} 1 \\ \frac{3}{2} \\ 2 \end{pmatrix} \\ z = 2\lambda + 3 \end{array}$$

NOTE

Again this set of equations is different from but equivalent to the earlier equations. The equivalence is most easily seen by substituting $2\mu - 1$ for λ, obtaining

$$x = 2\mu - 1$$
$$y = \frac{3}{2}(2\mu - 1) - \frac{9}{2} = 3\mu - 6$$
$$z = 2(2\mu - 1) + 3 = 4\mu + 1$$

Notice that Cartesian equations of a line, such as $\dfrac{x-1}{5} = \dfrac{y-3}{7} = \dfrac{z-4}{2}$,
are equivalent to the pair of equations

$$\frac{x-1}{5} = \frac{y-3}{7} \quad \text{and} \quad \frac{y-3}{7} = \frac{z-4}{2}$$

These can be rearranged as $\left\{\begin{array}{l} 7x - 5y = -8 \\ 2y - 7z = -22 \end{array}\right.$ which are the equations of

planes. You can always convert the Cartesian equations of a line into the equations of two planes. Every straight line may be regarded as the intersection of two planes.

Angle between two planes

The angle between two planes can be found by using the scalar product. As figures 5.5 and 5.6 make clear, the angle between planes π_1 and π_2 is the same as the angle between their normals, $\mathbf{n}_1$ and $\mathbf{n}_2$.

Figure 5.5

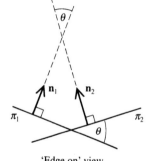

'Edge on' view

Figure 5.6

EXAMPLE

Find the acute angle between the planes π_1: $2x + 3y + 5z = 8$ and π_2: $5x + y - 4z = 12$.

Solution

The planes have normals $\mathbf{n}_1 = \begin{pmatrix} 2 \\ 3 \\ 5 \end{pmatrix}$ and $\mathbf{n}_2 = \begin{pmatrix} 5 \\ 1 \\ -4 \end{pmatrix}$, so $\mathbf{n}_1.\mathbf{n}_2 = 10 + 3 - 20 = -7$.

The angle between the normals is θ, where

$$\cos\theta = \frac{\mathbf{n}_1.\mathbf{n}_2}{|\mathbf{n}_1||\mathbf{n}_2|} = \frac{-7}{\sqrt{38}\sqrt{42}} \quad \Rightarrow \quad \theta \approx 100°$$

Therefore the acute angle between the planes is about $80°$.

Sheaf of planes

Figure 5.7

When several planes share a common line the arrangement is known as a *sheaf of planes* (figure 5.7). Our next example shows how you can find the equation of a plane which contains the line l common to two given planes, π_1 and π_2, without having to find the equation of l itself, or any points on l.

EXAMPLE

Find the equation of the plane which passes through the point $(1, 2, 3)$ and contains the common line of the planes π_1: $2x + 2y + z + 3 = 0$ and π_2: $2x + 3y + z + 13 = 0$.

Solution

The equation

$$p(2x + 2y + z + 3) + q(2x + 3y + z + 13) = 0 \qquad \text{①}$$

can be re-arranged in the form $ax + by + cz + d = 0$, where not all of a, b, c, d are zero provided p and q are not both zero. Therefore equation ① represents a plane. Further, any point (x, y, z) which satisfies both π_1 and π_2 will also satisfy equation ①. Thus equation ① represents a plane containing the common line of planes π_1 and π_2. Substituting $(1, 2, 3)$ into ① gives

$$12p + 24q = 0 \quad \Leftrightarrow \quad p = -2q$$

The required equation is

$$-2q(2x + 2y + z + 3) + q(2x + 3y + z + 13) = 0$$

$$\Leftrightarrow \quad -q(2x + y + z - 7) = 0$$

so that the required plane has equation $2x + y + z - 7 = 0$.

For Discussion

Planes π_1 and π_2 have equations $a_1x + b_1y + c_1z + d_1 = 0$ and $a_2x + b_2y + c_2z + d_2 = 0$ respectively. Plane π_3 has equation

$$p(a_1x + b_1y + c_1z + d_1) + q(a_2x + b_2y + c_2z + d_2) = 0$$

How is π_3 related to π_1 and π_2 if π_1 and π_2 are parallel?

In Chapter 4 you will have seen one method of solving simultaneous equations in three unknowns. The following example illustrates an alternative procedure.

EXAMPLE

Planes π_1: $9x + 3y - 5z = 12$

π_2: $7x + 2y - 4z = 8$

π_3: $13x + 4y - 7z = 18$

meet at the point P. Plane π_4 contains the common line of planes π_1 and π_3; π_5 contains the common line of π_2 and π_3; both π_4 and π_5 pass through the origin, O.

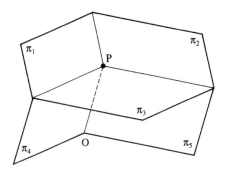

(i)   Find the equation of planes π_4 and π_5.

(ii) Find a vector parallel to both planes π_4 and π_5.

(iii) Hence find the co-ordinates of P.

Solution

(i) π_1: $9x + 3y - 5z = 12$ π_3: $13x + 4y - 7z = 18$

We find π_4 by adding multiples of π_1 and π_3.

As π_4 passes through the origin its 'constant term' is 0.

We eliminate the constant terms in π_1 and π_3 by calculating $3\pi_1 - 2\pi_3$, getting π_4: $x + y - z = 0$

Eliminating the constant terms in π_2: $7x + 2y - 4z = 8$

and π_3: $13x + 4y - 7z = 18$

by calculating $9\pi_2 - 4\pi_3$ gives π_5: $11x + 2y - 8z = 0$

(ii) Using $\mathbf{n}_4$ and $\mathbf{n}_5$ to represent the normals to π_4 and π_5, a vector parallel to both these planes will be

$$\mathbf{n}_4 \times \mathbf{n}_5 = \begin{pmatrix} 1 \\ 1 \\ -1 \end{pmatrix} \times \begin{pmatrix} 11 \\ 2 \\ -8 \end{pmatrix} = \begin{pmatrix} -6 \\ -3 \\ -9 \end{pmatrix} = -3 \begin{pmatrix} 2 \\ 1 \\ 3 \end{pmatrix}$$

(iii) The vector $\begin{pmatrix} 2 \\ 1 \\ 3 \end{pmatrix}$ is parallel to both π_4 and π_5, and is therefore parallel

to their common line, OP, so that $\overrightarrow{OP} = \lambda \begin{pmatrix} 2 \\ 1 \\ 3 \end{pmatrix}$ for some λ, and P has

co-ordinates $(2\lambda, \lambda, 3\lambda)$. Substituting these into the equation for π_3 we obtain

$$13(2\lambda) + 4\lambda - 7(3\lambda) = 18 \quad \Leftrightarrow \quad 9\lambda = 18$$

so that $\lambda = 2$, and P has co-ordinates $(4, 2, 6)$.

Exercise 5B

1. Find Cartesian equations of the line of intersection of the pairs of planes

(a) $x + y - 6z = 4$, $5x - 2y - 3z = 13$

(b) $5x - y + z = 8$, $x + 3y + z = -4$

(c) $3x + 2y - 6z = 4$, $x + 5y - 7z = 2$

(d) $5x + 2y - 3z = -2$, $3x - 3y - z = 2$

2. Find the acute angle between the pairs of planes in Question 1.

3. Find Cartesian equations of the line which passes through the given point and which is parallel to the line of intersection of the two planes

(a) $(-2, 3, 5)$, $4x - y + 3z = 5$, $3x - y + 2z = 7$

(b) $(4, -3, 2)$, $2x + 3y + 2z = 6$, $4x - 3y + z = 11$

4. Find the equation of the plane which goes through $(3, 2, -2)$ and which contains the common line of $x + 7y - 2z - 3 = 0$ and $2x - 3y + 2z - 1 = 0$.

5. Find the equation of the plane which contains the point $(1, -2, 3)$ and which is perpendicular to the common line of $5x - 3y - 4z = 2$ and $2x + y + 5z = 7$.

Exercise 5B continued

6. Find the equation of the line which goes through $(4, -2, -7)$ and which is parallel to both $2x - 5y - 2z = 8$ and $x + 3y - 3z = 12$.

7. The diagram shows the co-ordinates of the corners of parts of the roof of a warehouse.

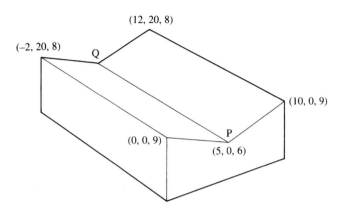

Find the equations of both roof sections, and the vector equation of the line PQ. Assuming that the z axis is vertical, what angle does PQ make with the horizontal?

8. Test drilling in the Namibian desert has shown the existence of gold deposits at $(400, 0, -400)$, $(-50, 500, -250)$, $(-200, -100, -200)$, where the units are in metres, the x axis points east, the y axis points north, and the z axis points up. Assume that these deposits are part of the same seam, contained in plane π.

(i) Find the equation of plane π.

(ii) Find the angle at which π is tilted to the horizontal.

The drilling positions $(400, 0, 3)$, $(-50, 500, 7)$, $(-200, -100, 5)$ are on the desert floor. Take the desert floor as a plane, Π.

(iii) Find the equation of Π.

(iv) Find the equation of the line where the plane containing the gold seam intersects the desert floor.

(v) How far south of the origin does the line found in part (d) pass?

9. Find the common point of the following sets of planes.

(a) $x + 3y + 2z = -7$, $3x + 5y + 4z = -7$, $x + 2y + z = -5$

(b) $9x - 3y - z = -4$, $x - 3y + z = 12$, $7x - 4y - 3z = -7$

(c) $6x + 9y + 5z = 17$, $5x - 8y - z = 40$, $9x - 2y - 8z = 41$

10. What happens if you attempt to use the method of the example on page 147 to find the common point of the following planes?

$$x + 2y + z = 10 \qquad 2x - y + 3z = 20 \qquad 3x + y + 4z = 30$$

Exercise 5B continued

11. Planes π_1 and π_2 have common line l and equations $2x + 2y + z + 7 = 0$ and $3x + 6y + 2z - 5 = 0$ respectively. Consider the equation

$$\lambda(2x + 2y + z + 7) + \mu(3x + 6y + 2z - 5) = 0 \qquad \text{①}$$

where λ and μ are not both zero.

(i) Explain why equation ① (a) represents the equation of a plane, (b) is satisfied by all points on l.

(ii) Describe the plane we get if (a) $\lambda = 0$, (b) $\mu = 0$.

Let $P(X, Y, Z)$ be any point on neither π_1 nor π_2.

(iii) Explain why $2X + 2Y + Z + 7 \neq 0$, and why $3X + 6Y + 2Z - 5 \neq 0$, but why there exist λ and μ (not both zero) such that

$$\lambda(2X + 2Y + Z + 7) + \mu(3X + 6Y + 2Z - 5) = 0$$

(iv) Complete the proof that all planes containing l can have their equations written in the form of equation ①.

The intersection of lines

Hold a pen and a pencil to represent two distinct straight lines as follows:

● hold them to represent parallel lines;

● hold them to represent intersecting lines;

● hold them to represent lines which are not parallel and which do not intersect (even if you extend them).

In three-dimensional space two or more straight lines which are not parallel and which do not meet are known as *skew* lines. In a plane two distinct lines are either parallel or intersecting, but in three dimensions there are three possibilities: the lines may be parallel, or intersecting, or skew. The next example illustrates a method of finding whether two lines meet, and if they do meet, the co-ordinates of the intersection point. A very similar method can be used if the lines are specified by their vector equations instead of their Cartesian equations.

EXAMPLE The lines l_1 and l_2 are represented by the equations

$$l_1 : \frac{x-1}{1} = \frac{y+6}{2} = \frac{z+1}{3} \qquad l_2 : \frac{x-9}{2} = \frac{y-7}{3} = \frac{z-2}{-1}$$

Find whether the lines meet, and, if so, the co-ordinates of their common point.

Solution

If there is a point (X, Y, Z) common to both lines then

$$\frac{X-1}{1} = \frac{Y+6}{2} = \frac{Z+1}{3} = \lambda, \text{say, and} \quad \frac{X-9}{2} = \frac{Y-7}{3} = \frac{Z-2}{-1} = \mu, \text{say.}$$

Writing X, Y and Z in terms of the parameters λ and μ, gives

$$X = \lambda + 1 = 2\mu + 9 \qquad \qquad ①$$

$$Y = 2\lambda - 6 = 3\mu + 7 \qquad \qquad ②$$

$$Z = 3\lambda - 1 = -\mu + 2 \qquad \qquad ③$$

Now solve any two of the three equations above simultaneously.

In this example we use ① and ②:

$$\left. \begin{array}{r} \lambda - 2\mu = 8 \\ 2\lambda - 3\mu = 13 \end{array} \right\} \Leftrightarrow \left\{ \begin{array}{r} 2\lambda - 4\mu = 16 \\ 2\lambda - 3\mu = 13 \end{array} \right\} \Leftrightarrow \mu = -3, \lambda = 2$$

If these solutions satisfy the previously unused equation (equation ③ here) then the lines do meet, and our value of λ (or value of μ) substituted into equations ①, ② and ③ gives us the co-ordinates (X, Y, Z) of the common point.

If our values of λ and μ do not fit the third (previously unused) equation then the lines do not meet.

As $\lambda = 2 \Rightarrow Z = 3\lambda - 1 = 5$ and $\mu = -3 \Rightarrow Z = -\mu + 2 = 5$, the values $\lambda = 2$ and $\mu = -3$ satisfy equation ③, as well as equations ① and ②, proving that the lines meet.

Using $\lambda = 2$ or $\mu = -3$ in equations ①, ② and ③ gives $X = 3$, $Y = -2$, $Z = 5$. The lines meet at the point $(3, -2, 5)$.

The Cartesian equations of line ℓ_2 in the last example were

$$\frac{x-9}{2} = \frac{y-7}{3} = \frac{z-2}{-1}$$

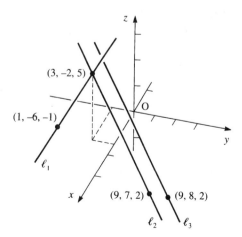

Figure 5.8

If we replace $y - 7$ by $y - 8$ in the equations, we translate line l_2 one unit parallel to the y axis, forming line l_3 (figure 5.8). We do not expect lines l_1 and l_3 to intersect.

EXAMPLE

Prove that the lines l_1 and l_3 do not meet, where

$$\ell_1: \frac{x-1}{1} = \frac{y+6}{2} = \frac{z+1}{3} \qquad \ell_3: \frac{x-9}{2} = \frac{y-8}{3} = \frac{z-2}{-1}.$$

Solution

If there is a point (X, Y, Z) common to both lines then

$$\frac{X-1}{1} = \frac{Y+6}{2} = \frac{Z+1}{3} = \lambda, \text{say, and } \frac{X-9}{2} = \frac{Y-8}{3} = \frac{Z-2}{-1} = \mu \text{ say.}$$

Writing X, Y and Z in terms of the parameters λ and μ:

$$X = \lambda + 1 = 2\mu + 9 \qquad \text{①}$$
$$Y = 2\lambda - 6 = 3\mu + 8 \qquad \text{②}$$
$$Z = 3\lambda - 1 = -\mu + 2 \qquad \text{③}$$

Solving equations ① and ② simultaneously:

$$\begin{cases} \lambda - 2\mu = 8 \\ 2\lambda - 3\mu = 14 \end{cases} \Leftrightarrow \begin{cases} 2\lambda - 4\mu = 16 \\ 2\lambda - 3\mu = 14 \end{cases} \Leftrightarrow \mu = -2, \ \lambda = 4.$$

As $\lambda = 4 \Rightarrow Z = 3\lambda - 1 = 11$, but $\mu = -2 \Rightarrow Z = -\mu + 2 = 4$, the values $\lambda = 4$ and $\mu = -2$ do not satisfy equation ③, although they satisfy equations ① and ②, proving that these lines do not meet.

Exercise 5C

1. Decide whether the following pairs of lines intersect or not. If they do intersect, find the co-ordinates of the intersection point.

(a) $\frac{x-6}{1} = \frac{y+4}{-2} = \frac{z-2}{5}, \quad \frac{x-1}{1} = \frac{y-4}{-1} = \frac{z+17}{2}$

(b) $\frac{x+1}{2} = \frac{y-2}{0} = \frac{z-4}{3}, \quad \frac{x+4}{5} = \frac{y-4}{-2} = \frac{z-6}{1}$

(c) $\frac{x}{5} = \frac{y+1}{3} = \frac{z-4}{-3}, \quad \frac{x-2}{4} = \frac{y-5}{-3} = \frac{z+1}{2}$

(d) $\mathbf{r} = \begin{pmatrix} 9 \\ 3 \\ -4 \end{pmatrix} + t\begin{pmatrix} 1 \\ 2 \\ -3 \end{pmatrix}, \quad \mathbf{r} = \begin{pmatrix} 1 \\ -4 \\ 5 \end{pmatrix} + t\begin{pmatrix} 1 \\ -1 \\ 2 \end{pmatrix}$

(e) $\mathbf{r} = \begin{pmatrix} 2 \\ 3 \\ 1 \end{pmatrix} + t\begin{pmatrix} 1 \\ 1 \\ -2 \end{pmatrix}, \quad \mathbf{r} = \begin{pmatrix} -1 \\ -3 \\ -1 \end{pmatrix} + t\begin{pmatrix} 1 \\ 3 \\ 2 \end{pmatrix}$

Pure Mathematics 4

P4   152

2. To support a tree damaged in a gale a tree surgeon attaches wire guys to four of the branches (see diagram). He joins $(2, 0, 3)$ to $(-1, 2, 6)$ and $(0, 3, 5)$ to $(-2, -2, 4)$. Do the guys, assumed straight, meet?

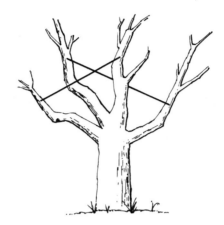

3. The line with Cartesian equations $\dfrac{x+4}{2} = \dfrac{y-4}{-10} = \dfrac{z+12}{11}$ meets

$\dfrac{x-4}{2} = \dfrac{y+15}{-3} = \dfrac{z+16}{-5}$ at A and meets $\dfrac{x+1}{1} = \dfrac{y+29}{1} = \dfrac{z+3}{8}$ at B. Find the co-ordinates of A and the length of AB.

4. Show that the three lines $\dfrac{x+7}{4} = \dfrac{y-24}{-7} = \dfrac{z+4}{4}$, $\dfrac{x-3}{2} = \dfrac{y+10}{2} = \dfrac{z-15}{-1}$,

$\dfrac{x+3}{8} = \dfrac{y-6}{-3} = \dfrac{z-6}{2}$ form a triangle, and find the lengths of its sides.

5. A triangle has its vertices at A$(7, 5, -3)$, B$(8, -3, 1)$ and C$(5, 6, -1)$. Find $\overrightarrow{AB}$ and $\overrightarrow{AC}$ and explain why the vector $\overrightarrow{AB} + 3\overrightarrow{AC}$ is parallel to the bisector of angle BAC. Find the co-ordinates of the point where the bisector of angle BAC meets BC.

6. The bisectors of the angles of a triangle meet at a point which is known as the *incentre*. The incentre is the centre of the largest circle which fits inside the triangle. Find the incentre of triangle ABC when A is at the point $(3, 4, -5)$, B is at $(3, 4, 6)$ and C is at $(7, 12, -13)$.

7. Lines l and l' are skew, and X is a point on neither l nor l'. By considering the plane containing both l and X, or otherwise, prove that if there is a line through X intersecting both l and l', then it is unique.

8. (i) Show that the lines $\ell_1 : \dfrac{x+1}{3} = \dfrac{y+4}{-4} = \dfrac{z-5}{7}$ and $\ell_2 : \dfrac{x-12}{0} = \dfrac{y}{2} = \dfrac{z-2}{-3}$

are skew (see diagram on page 154).

Exercise 5C continued

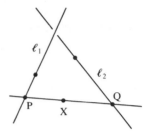

(ii) The points P and Q are on lines ℓ_1 and ℓ_2 respectively. Write down the co-ordinates of P and Q in terms of parameters p and q respectively.

(iii) The line PQ passes through the point X(8, 6, –8). Use the fact that $\overrightarrow{XP} = \lambda\overrightarrow{XQ}$ to find the equation of PQ (in any form).

(iv) Find the co-ordinates of P and Q.

9. (i) A cube has side a. Show that the vertices are $\frac{1}{2}a\sqrt{3}$ from the centre of the cube.

(ii) Points A and B have co-ordinates (3, 3, 3) and (5, –1, –1) respectively. Show that OA = OB = $\frac{1}{2}\sqrt{3}$ AB.

(iii) A and B are adjacent vertices of a cube which has its centre at the origin. Find the co-ordinates of the other vertices.

10. (i) Show that the lines $\ell_1 : \dfrac{x-11}{2} = \dfrac{y+9}{1} = \dfrac{z-25}{2}$ and $\ell_2 : \dfrac{x-4}{2} = \dfrac{y-15}{-6} = \dfrac{z-5}{-5}$ are skew.

(ii) The points P and Q are on lines ℓ_1 and ℓ_2 respectively, such that PQ is perpendicular to both ℓ_1 and ℓ_2. Find a vector parallel to PQ and a vector perpendicular to both PQ and ℓ_2.

(iii) Find the equation of the plane π that contains both PQ and ℓ_2.

(iv) Find where ℓ_1 meets π.

(v) Find the Cartesian equations of PQ.

(vi) Find the co-ordinates of Q and the shortest distance between lines ℓ_1 and ℓ_2.

11. In a chemical plant a straight pipe connects A(–2, 32, –3) and B(23, 57, –23) and a second straight pipe connects C(25, 3, 14) and D(49, 30, –1), where axes are scaled in metres. Use the methods described in Question 10 to find the length of the shortest straight pipe that would connect AB to CD, and the co-ordinates of the necessary junction points.

The scalar triple product

With this brief account of the scalar triple product we tidy up some loose ends from earlier sections; a full treatment is given in Pure Mathematics 6.

In parallelogram OACB, the sides OA and OB are represented by vectors **a** and **b** (figure 5.9).

Figure 5.9

The area of the parallelogram is OA × OB sin θ which is the magnitude of **a** × **b**.

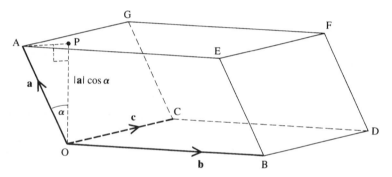

Figure 5.10

A parallelepiped is a polyhedron with six faces each of which is a parallelogram.

The volume V of any parallelepiped is the product of the base area and the height. In parallelepiped OBDCAEFG (figure 5.10) take parallelogram OBDC as the base; it has area |**b** × **c**|. The height of the parallelepiped is OP, where P is the foot of the perpendicular from O to plane AEFG.

If angle AOP is α, the length of OP is |**a**| cos α, and the volume of parallelepiped OBDCAEFG is $V =$ |**a**||**b** × **c**| cos α.

If, as illustrated in figure 5.10, **a, b, c** is a right-handed set of vectors, **b** × **c** has the same sense as $\overrightarrow{OP}$, and |**a**||**b** × **c**| cos α = **a**.(**b** × **c**); in this case V = **a**.(**b** × **c**).

However, if **a, b, c** is left-handed, **b** × **c** and $\overrightarrow{OP}$ are parallel but with opposite sense; in this case the angle between **a** and **b** × **c** is $\pi - \alpha$, which is obtuse, so that V = |**a**||**b** × **c**| cos α = −**a**.(**b** × **c**).

Thus **a**.(**b** × **c**) is the signed volume of the parallelepiped with edges represented by **a, b** and **c**.

As the volume of the parallelepiped does not depend on which parallelogram we take as the base,

$$\mathbf{a}.(\mathbf{b} \times \mathbf{c}) = \mathbf{b}.(\mathbf{c} \times \mathbf{a}) = \mathbf{c}.(\mathbf{a} \times \mathbf{b})$$
$$= -\mathbf{a}.(\mathbf{c} \times \mathbf{b}) = -\mathbf{b}.(\mathbf{a} \times \mathbf{c}) = -\mathbf{c}.(\mathbf{b} \times \mathbf{a})$$

The scalar $\mathbf{a}.(\mathbf{b} \times \mathbf{c})$ is called the *scalar triple product* of $\mathbf{a}, \mathbf{b}, \mathbf{c}$. Cyclic interchange of the letters does not affect the value of the scalar triple product, but non-cyclic interchange of the letters multiplies the product by -1.

We can now prove the distributive property of vector product over vector addition. Let $\mathbf{e}$ be an arbitrary unit vector. Then

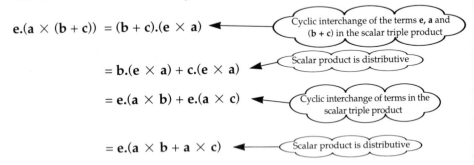

$$\mathbf{e}.(\mathbf{a} \times (\mathbf{b} + \mathbf{c})) = (\mathbf{b} + \mathbf{c}).(\mathbf{e} \times \mathbf{a}) \qquad \text{Cyclic interchange of the terms } \mathbf{e}, \mathbf{a} \text{ and } (\mathbf{b} + \mathbf{c}) \text{ in the scalar triple product}$$

$$= \mathbf{b}.(\mathbf{e} \times \mathbf{a}) + \mathbf{c}.(\mathbf{e} \times \mathbf{a}) \qquad \text{Scalar product is distributive}$$

$$= \mathbf{e}.(\mathbf{a} \times \mathbf{b}) + \mathbf{e}.(\mathbf{a} \times \mathbf{c}) \qquad \text{Cyclic interchange of terms in the scalar triple product}$$

$$= \mathbf{e}.(\mathbf{a} \times \mathbf{b} + \mathbf{a} \times \mathbf{c}) \qquad \text{Scalar product is distributive}$$

Since $\mathbf{e}$ is any unit vector we may replace $\mathbf{e}$ with $\mathbf{i}$:

$$\mathbf{i}.(\mathbf{a} \times (\mathbf{b} + \mathbf{c})) = \mathbf{i}.(\mathbf{a} \times \mathbf{b} + \mathbf{a} \times \mathbf{c})$$

This means that the $\mathbf{i}$ components of the two vectors $\mathbf{a} \times (\mathbf{b} + \mathbf{c})$ and $\mathbf{a} \times \mathbf{b} + \mathbf{a} \times \mathbf{c}$ are equal. A similar argument shows that the $\mathbf{j}$ components of $\mathbf{a} \times (\mathbf{b} + \mathbf{c})$ and $\mathbf{a} \times \mathbf{b} + \mathbf{a} \times \mathbf{c}$ are equal, and that their $\mathbf{k}$ components are also equal. Thus

$$\mathbf{a} \times (\mathbf{b} + \mathbf{c}) = \mathbf{a} \times \mathbf{b} + \mathbf{a} \times \mathbf{c}$$

In Chapter 4 you met the determinant, det $\mathbf{M}$, of the 2×2 matrix $\mathbf{M} = \begin{pmatrix} a & c \\ b & d \end{pmatrix}$;

det $\mathbf{M} = ad - bc$, the (signed) area scale factor of the transformation represented by matrix $\mathbf{M}$. This transformation (figure 5.11) maps the unit square into parallelogram OPQR, where $\overrightarrow{OP} = \begin{pmatrix} a \\ b \end{pmatrix}$ and $\overrightarrow{OR} = \begin{pmatrix} c \\ d \end{pmatrix}$.

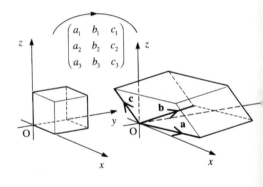

Figure 5.11

In just the same way the 3 × 3 matrix $\mathbf{N} = \begin{pmatrix} a_1 & b_1 & c_1 \\ a_2 & b_2 & c_2 \\ a_3 & b_3 & c_3 \end{pmatrix}$ transforms the unit

cube into a parallelepiped with edges given by vectors

$$\mathbf{a} = \begin{pmatrix} a_1 \\ a_2 \\ a_3 \end{pmatrix} \quad \mathbf{b} = \begin{pmatrix} b_1 \\ b_2 \\ b_3 \end{pmatrix} \quad \mathbf{c} = \begin{pmatrix} c_1 \\ c_2 \\ c_3 \end{pmatrix}$$

The scalar $\mathbf{a}.(\mathbf{b} \times \mathbf{c})$ is the (signed) volume of this parallelepiped; this is defined as the determinant of the 3 × 3 matrix $\mathbf{N}$, and is denoted by both

$\det \mathbf{N}$ and $\begin{vmatrix} a_1 & b_1 & c_1 \\ a_2 & b_2 & c_2 \\ a_3 & b_3 & c_3 \end{vmatrix}$. We thus have

$$\det \mathbf{N} = \begin{vmatrix} a_1 & b_1 & c_1 \\ a_2 & b_2 & c_2 \\ a_3 & b_3 & c_3 \end{vmatrix} = \mathbf{a}.(\mathbf{b} \times \mathbf{c})$$

$$= \begin{pmatrix} a_1 \\ a_2 \\ a_3 \end{pmatrix}.\left(\begin{pmatrix} b_1 \\ b_2 \\ b_3 \end{pmatrix} \times \begin{pmatrix} c_1 \\ c_2 \\ c_3 \end{pmatrix} \right)$$

$$= \begin{pmatrix} a_1 \\ a_2 \\ a_3 \end{pmatrix}.\left(\begin{vmatrix} b_2 & c_2 \\ b_3 & c_3 \end{vmatrix}\mathbf{i} - \begin{vmatrix} b_1 & c_1 \\ b_3 & c_3 \end{vmatrix}\mathbf{j} + \begin{vmatrix} b_1 & c_1 \\ b_2 & c_2 \end{vmatrix}\mathbf{k} \right)$$

$$= a_1\begin{vmatrix} b_2 & c_2 \\ b_3 & c_3 \end{vmatrix} - a_2\begin{vmatrix} b_1 & c_1 \\ b_3 & c_3 \end{vmatrix} + a_3\begin{vmatrix} b_1 & c_1 \\ b_2 & c_2 \end{vmatrix}$$

The expansion of the 3 × 3 determinant in terms of 2 × 2 determinants has a form similar to the expression for $\mathbf{a} \times \mathbf{b}$ in terms of 2 × 2 determinants. For this reason the vector product is sometimes written in the form of a 3 × 3 determinant:

$$\mathbf{a} \times \mathbf{b} = \begin{pmatrix} a_1 \\ a_2 \\ a_3 \end{pmatrix} \times \begin{pmatrix} b_1 \\ b_2 \\ b_3 \end{pmatrix} = \begin{vmatrix} \mathbf{i} & a_1 & b_1 \\ \mathbf{j} & a_2 & b_2 \\ \mathbf{k} & a_3 & b_3 \end{vmatrix}$$

EXAMPLE Evaluate the determinant $\begin{vmatrix} 2 & -1 & -2 \\ 3 & 7 & 6 \\ 5 & 4 & 9 \end{vmatrix}$.

Solution

$$\begin{vmatrix} 2 & -1 & -2 \\ 3 & 7 & 6 \\ 5 & 4 & 9 \end{vmatrix} = 2\begin{vmatrix} 7 & 6 \\ 4 & 9 \end{vmatrix} - 3\begin{vmatrix} -1 & -2 \\ 4 & 9 \end{vmatrix} + 5\begin{vmatrix} -1 & -2 \\ 7 & 6 \end{vmatrix}$$

$$= 2(7 \times 9 - 4 \times 6) - 3[(-1) \times 9 - 4 \times (-2)] + 5[(-1) \times 6 - 7 \times (-2)]$$

$$= 2 \times 39 - 3 \times (-1) + 5 \times 8$$

$$= 121$$

For Discussion

Are the brackets in the scalar triple product a.(b × c) necessary?

Exercise 5D

1. Evaluate

(a) $\begin{vmatrix} 2 & 3 & 4 \\ 1 & 2 & 1 \\ 3 & 5 & 3 \end{vmatrix}$ (b) $\begin{vmatrix} 1 & 4 & 3 \\ 1 & -2 & -4 \\ -5 & 3 & 7 \end{vmatrix}$ (c) $\begin{vmatrix} 1 & 4 & 7 \\ 2 & 5 & 8 \\ 3 & 6 & 9 \end{vmatrix}$ (d) $\begin{vmatrix} 5 & 5 & -1 \\ 3 & 0 & 2 \\ 1 & -3 & 1 \end{vmatrix}$

2. (a) Show that a.(b × c) = 0 ⇔ O, A, B, C are coplanar.

(b) Show that P(2, –7, 0), Q(8, –6, 4), R(–3, 38, 5) and the origin are coplanar.

(c) Decide whether W(4, 1, 1), X(3, –3, –2), Y(2, 0, –3) and Z(5, –2, 2) are coplanar.

3. P and Q are the points (2, 5, 1) and (4, 3, 2) respectively. R and S are further points such that PQRS is a parallelogram with $\overrightarrow{QR}$ = –i + 2j + 3k. Find the co-ordinates of R and S and the area of PQRS.

4. (i) Explain why the area of triangle ABC is $\frac{1}{2}|(c-a) \times (b-a)|$.

(ii) Show that the formula in part (i) simplifies to $\frac{1}{2}|a \times b + b \times c + c \times a|$.

(iii) Use the formula in part (i) to find the area of the triangle which has vertices at A(–3, –2), B(5, 1) and C(–6, 3).

[Hint: Work in three dimensions taking (–3, –2) as (–3, –2, 0).]

(iv) Check your answer to part (iii) by finding the area of the surrounding rectangle and subtracting the area of three right-angled triangles (see diagram).

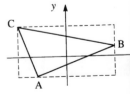

(v) Explain why it is usually easier to use the formula in part (i) rather than the formula in part (ii).

5. Show that a + b + c = 0 ⇒ a × b = b × c = c × a. Is the converse true?

Investigations

1. Redefine a vector as an $n \times 1$ matrix. We now also need to redefine properties such as magnitude and scalar product, and some of these lose their obvious physical significance.

   (i) Suggest possible definitions for magnitude and scalar product of vectors like $\begin{pmatrix} 2 \\ 2 \\ 4 \\ 1 \end{pmatrix}$.

   (ii) Find the angle between the vectors $\begin{pmatrix} 2 \\ 2 \\ 4 \\ 1 \end{pmatrix}$ and $\begin{pmatrix} 2 \\ 3 \\ -8 \\ 2 \end{pmatrix}$.

   (iii) Investigate vectors which are perpendicular both to $\begin{pmatrix} 2 \\ 2 \\ 4 \\ 1 \end{pmatrix}$ and $\begin{pmatrix} 2 \\ 3 \\ -8 \\ 2 \end{pmatrix}$.

2. *The vector triple product* of **a**, **b** and **c** is the vector $\mathbf{a} \times (\mathbf{b} \times \mathbf{c})$. Is $\mathbf{a} \times (\mathbf{b} \times \mathbf{c}) = (\mathbf{a} \times \mathbf{b}) \times \mathbf{c}$?

   Investigate other properties of the vector triple product.

KEY POINTS

- The vector product of **a** and **b** is $\mathbf{a} \times \mathbf{b} = |\mathbf{a}||\mathbf{b}| \sin\theta\, \hat{\mathbf{n}}$, where θ is the angle between **a** and **b**, and $\hat{\mathbf{n}}$ is a unit vector which is perpendicular to both **a** and **b**.

- $\mathbf{a} \times \mathbf{b} = \begin{pmatrix} a_1 \\ a_2 \\ a_3 \end{pmatrix} \times \begin{pmatrix} b_1 \\ b_2 \\ b_3 \end{pmatrix} = \begin{vmatrix} \mathbf{i} & a_1 & b_1 \\ \mathbf{j} & a_2 & b_2 \\ \mathbf{k} & a_3 & b_3 \end{vmatrix} = \begin{pmatrix} a_2 b_3 - a_3 b_2 \\ a_3 b_1 - a_1 b_3 \\ a_1 b_2 - a_2 b_1 \end{pmatrix}$.

- The vector product is anti-commutative:
  $$\mathbf{a} \times \mathbf{b} = -\mathbf{b} \times \mathbf{a}$$
  and distributive over vector addition:
  $$\mathbf{a} \times (\mathbf{b} + \mathbf{c}) = \mathbf{a} \times \mathbf{b} + \mathbf{a} \times \mathbf{c}$$

- To find the equations of ℓ, the line of intersection of the planes

$$a_1x + a_2y + a_3z = a_4 \quad \text{and} \quad b_1x + b_2y + b_3z = b_4$$

(a) find a point P on ℓ by choosing a value for one of x, y, or z, substituting this into both equations, and then solving simultaneously to find the other two variables;

(b) *either* find a second point Q on ℓ, as in (a) and use $\overrightarrow{PQ}$ as **d**, the direction vector of ℓ

    or   use $\mathbf{a} \times \mathbf{b}$ as **d**, the direction vector of ℓ, where

$$\mathbf{a} = \begin{pmatrix} a_1 \\ a_2 \\ a_3 \end{pmatrix} \quad \text{and} \quad \mathbf{b} = \begin{pmatrix} b_1 \\ b_2 \\ b_3 \end{pmatrix}$$

are the normals to the two planes;

(c) then write down the vector equation or the Cartesian equations of ℓ.

- The angle between two planes is the same as the angle between their normals.

- To find the intersection point of the lines

$$\frac{x - x_1}{d_1} = \frac{y - y_1}{e_1} = \frac{z - z_1}{f_1} \quad \text{and} \quad \frac{x - x_2}{d_2} = \frac{y - y_2}{e_2} = \frac{z - z_2}{f_2}$$

(a) express the co-ordinates of points on the lines in terms of parameters λ and μ:

$$x = d_1\lambda + x_1 = d_2\mu + x_2$$
$$y = e_1\lambda + y_1 = e_2\mu + y_2$$
$$z = f_1\lambda + z_1 = f_2\mu + z_2$$

(b) solve two of the equations simultaneously for λ and μ, and check whether the solution satisfies the third equation;

(c) if the values found for λ and μ satisfy all three equations the corresponding values of x, y, z are the co-ordinates of the point where the lines intersect;

if the values found for λ and μ do not satisfy the third equation the lines do not intersect.

Answers

Exercise 1A

1. (a) $\Rightarrow$ (b) $\Leftarrow$ (c) $\Leftarrow$ (d) $\Leftrightarrow$ (e) $\Rightarrow$ (f) $\Leftrightarrow$ **2.** (i) correct (ii) Q only if P (iii) P if S
(iv) R if and only if P (v) correct (vi) Q only if R. **3.** I did not have to go to school.
4. (a) necessary (b) necessary and sufficient (c) sufficient (d) neither
5. (a) For a polynomial $P(x)$, if $(x-a)$ is a factor of $P(x)$ then $P(a) = 0$. True.
(b) If a solid has a uniform cross-section then the solid is a prism. False (e.g twisted prism).
(c) If $a^2 = b^2 + c^2$ then triangle ABC has a right angle at A. True.
(d) If $\dfrac{dy}{dx} = nx^{n-1}$ then $y = x^n$. False (e.g. $y = x^n + 1$). **6.** (i) neither (ii) necessary (iii) sufficient
(iv) necessary and sufficient. **7.** q is the form of $2^a 5^b$ **8.** 5 **9.** 3 **10.** No solution

Exercise 1B

1. $(3k \pm 1)^2 = 3(3k^2 \pm 2k) + 1$, which is not a multiple of 3.
3. (i) If not then rational + irrational = rational, so irrational = rational − rational = rational.
Contradiction. (ii) Counter example: $(3 - \sqrt{2}) + \sqrt{2} = 3$, which is rational
(iii) Proof as in (i) with $\times$ and $\div$ in place of + and −. (iv) Counter example: $\sqrt{2} \times \sqrt{8} = 4$.
5. Suppose the line goes from left to right. Consider removing each green segment together with its right-hand end point.
6. (i) Show that at least three of the segments ending at a particular point are of the same colour. Consider the triangle formed by joining the other end points of three such segments.
(ii) Green pentagon with yellow diagonals.
9. (ii) type A $\times$ type B = type B; type B $\times$ type B = type A (iv) 5, 13, 17, ...; 3, 7, 11, ...
(vi) In fact there are infinitely many primes of type A, but no easy proof of this seems to be known.

Exercise 1C

1. n^2 **2.** $\dfrac{n(3n+5)}{2}$ **3.** $\dfrac{n}{n+1}$ **4.** $\dfrac{n}{2n+1}$ **5.** $(n+1)! - 1$ **6.** $\dfrac{n+1}{2n}$ ($n \geqslant 2$) **7.** $\dfrac{1}{n}$ **8.** $3^n - 1$

12. 7 **13.** $n = 1$ or $n \geqslant 10$ **14.** (i) $r_n = n + 1$ (iii) $t_n = \frac{1}{6}n(n^2 + 5) + 1$

Note that $r_n = \binom{n}{1} + \binom{n}{0}$, $s_n = \binom{n}{2} + \binom{n}{1} + \binom{n}{0}$, $t_n = \binom{n}{3} + \binom{n}{2} + \binom{n}{1} + \binom{n}{0}$.

A direct proof (for t_n say) can be obtained by turning the configuration so that none of the planes or their lines of intersection is horizontal (how can you be sure that this is always possible?) and then counting (a) the regions which have a lowest point, and (b) the regions with no lowest point.
15. Always divisible by 7. **17.** (i) $u_n = 2$ (ii) $u_n = 4^{n-1} + 2$
19. Since $(3 - \sqrt{5})^n < 0.5$ for $n > 1$, u_n is the integer nearest to $(3 + \sqrt{5})^n$. Divisibility by 2^n comes from the recurrence relation by induction.
20. (i) f_n is even if and only if n is divisible by 3. (ii) $\displaystyle\sum_{r=1}^{n} f_r = f_{n+2} - 1$; $\displaystyle\sum_{r=1}^{n} f_{2r-1} = f_{2n}$; $\displaystyle\sum_{r=1}^{n} f_{2r} = f_{2n+1} - 1$
(iii) $f_n f_{n+3} - f_{n+1} f_{n+2} = (-1)^{n+1}$ (vi) For these properties, and much more,
see Chapter 1 of *Numbers and Shapes Revisited* by Judita Cofman (Oxford University Press, 1995).

Exercise 1D

1. n^2 **2.** $n(n+1)^2$ **3.** $\frac{1}{12}n(n+1)(n+2)(3n+1)$. **4.** n^4
5. $\frac{1}{4}(n+4)^2(n+5)^2 - 100 = \frac{1}{4}n(n+9)(n^2 + 9n + 40)$ **6.** $\frac{9}{2}n^2(3n^2 - 1)$ **7.** 7 **9.** $p = 1653, q = 1596$

10. $\dfrac{n(3n+5)}{4(n+1)(n+2)}$ **11.** $\dfrac{n(n+1)}{6(n+3)(n+4)}$ **12.** $\dfrac{n(n+3)}{4(n+1)(n+2)}$ **13.** $\dfrac{n(n+2)}{(n+1)^2}$

15. (i) $\frac{1}{4}n(n+1)(n+2)(n+3)$ (ii) $\dfrac{1}{k+2}n(n+1)(n+2)...(n+k+1)$ **17.** $\frac{1}{2} - \dfrac{1}{(n+1)2^{n+1}}$

18. $T = \dfrac{1-(n+1)x^n + nx^{n+1}}{(1-x)^2}$ **19.** $1 - \dfrac{x^n}{(x+1)(x+2)\ldots(x+n)}$

21. (i) $S_4 = \frac{1}{30}n(n+1)(2n+1)(3n^2+3n-1)$

Exercise 2A

1.

2.

3.

4.

5.

6.

7.

8.

9.

10.

11.

12.

13.

14.

15.

16.

17.

18.

19.

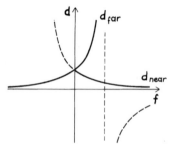

Maximum after 2 hours.

20.

21.

For $0 < u < c$, the gradient increases as f decreases.

22.

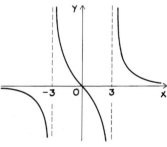

Small apertures (large f numbers) mean that a wide range of distances are in focus, suiting landscapes.

Large apertures cause small depth of field, isolating the subject from its surroundings, often suitable for portraits.

23.

(i) $-yx^2 - x - 9y = 0$
(ii)   2
(iii) y decreases from $+\infty$ to $-\infty$ monotonically.

24. $y = \dfrac{x-2}{x+3}$ is equivalent to a linear equation in x, so that there is at most one value of x for every given value of y.

25. If $a = c$ and $b < a$ there is a turning point to the left of $x = b$.

Exercise 2B

1.

2.

3.

4.

5.

6.

7.

8.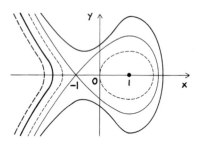

9. (i) $(0, \frac{2}{3})$; $(2, 0)$, $(-1, 0)$ (ii) $1 - \dfrac{4}{(x-3)^2}$; $(5, 9)$, $(1, 1)$ (iii) $y = x + 2$, oblique asymptote

(iv)

(v)

Exercise 2C

1.

2.

3.

4.

5.

6.

7.

Two roots

8.

Maximum at $\left(\frac{5}{2}, \frac{9}{25}\right)$

(i)

(ii)

Exercise 2D

1. $-3 < x < 1$ or $x > \frac{7}{2}$ **2.** $x < 1$ or $x > 3$ **3.** $x < -2$ or $0 < x < 5$ **4.** $x < -1$ or $2 \leqslant x \leqslant 5$

5. $-1 < x \leqslant \frac{2}{5}$ or $x > 2$ **6.** $-2 \leqslant x < 0$ or $x \geqslant 4$ **7.** $x < 3$ **8.** $x = 0$ or $1 \leqslant x < 2$ **9.** $-5 \leqslant x < 2$

10. $x < -6$ or $-2 \leqslant x < \frac{2}{3}$ **11.** $1 \leqslant x \leqslant 3$ **12.** $-5 \leqslant x \leqslant -\frac{1}{3}$ **13.** $x > \frac{2}{5}$ **14.** $-1 \leqslant x \leqslant 2$ or $4 \leqslant x \leqslant 7$

15. $1 \leqslant x \leqslant 3$ **16.** $x^2(y-1) + x + 2 = 0$; $8(y-1) \leqslant 1$; $y \leqslant \frac{9}{8}$ **18.** $-1 \leqslant y \leqslant 3$

Exercise 2E

1. (ii) When $p = q = r$ **4.** (ii) For example: true if $x = 1, y = -2$; false if $x = 2, y = -1$

9. (iii) Equality if and only if $x_1 = x_2 = \ldots = x_n$

Investigations: page 53

3. (v) $r = 1$ if and only if all points (x_i, y_i) lie on the same straight line with positive gradient.
$r = -1$ if and only if all points (x_i, y_i) lie on the same straight line with negative gradient.

Exercise 3A

1. $14 + 10j$ **2.** $5 + 2j$ **3.** $-3 + 4j$ **4.** $-1 + j$ **5.** 21 **6.** $12 + 21j$ **7.** $\frac{5}{6} + \frac{10}{3}j$ **8.** $\frac{11}{3} + \frac{23}{3}j$

9. $40 + 42j$ **10.** 100 **11.** $43 + 76j$ **12.** $-9 + 46j$

Exercise 3B

1. $\frac{3}{10} - \frac{1}{10}j$ 2. $\frac{6}{37} + \frac{1}{37}j$ 3. $-\frac{1}{4} + \frac{3}{4}j$ 4. $\frac{4}{5} + \frac{11}{10}j$ 5. $7 - 5j$ 6. $-1 - \frac{3}{2}j$ 7. (a) $z = 11 - 10j$

(b) $z = \frac{34}{5} + \frac{22}{5}j$, $w = \frac{44}{5} - \frac{33}{5}j$ 8. $a^3 - 3ab^2 + (3a^2b - b^3)j$; $z = 1$ or $\frac{-1 \pm \sqrt{3}j}{2}$ 9. (a) $-j$

(b) 1   (c) j (d) $-j$ (e) -1; $j^n = 1, j, -1, -j$ when $n = 4k, 4k + 1, 4k + 2, 4k + 3$ respectively

10. (i) (a) 0,   (b) -1,   (ii) $q - p + 1$ is a multiple of 4   11. (i) $ac - bd + (ad + bc)j$

12. (a) $\pm 4j$ (b) $-2 \pm 4j$ (c) $\frac{2 \pm 5j}{3}$;   (d) $2j, 3j$.   13. (b) (i) $z^2 - 14z + 65 = 0$; (ii) $9z^2 + 25 = 0$

(iii) $z^2 + 4z + 12 = 0$ (iv) $z^2 - (5 + 3j)z + 4 + 7j = 0$ 15. (i) $a = 5, b = 2$ (ii) $a = 3, b = -7$

(iii) $a = 1.25, b = -0.75$ (iv) $a = b = 1/\sqrt{2}$ 16. $a = -7, b = 11$; other solution is $z = 5 - 2j$

17. $2, 3 - j$ 18. (a) $(z + 2j)(z - 2j)$ (b) $(z + 3 + 2j)(z + 3 - 2j)$ (c) $(z + \frac{1}{2} + \frac{\sqrt{3}}{2}j)(z + \frac{1}{2} - \frac{\sqrt{3}}{2}j)$

(d) $(z + 1)(z - \frac{1}{2} + \frac{\sqrt{3}}{2}j)(z - \frac{1}{2} - \frac{\sqrt{3}}{2}j)$ (e) $(z + \frac{1}{\sqrt{2}} + \frac{1}{\sqrt{2}}j)(z + \frac{1}{\sqrt{2}} - \frac{1}{\sqrt{2}}j)(z$

$- \frac{1}{\sqrt{2}} + \frac{1}{\sqrt{2}}j)(z - \frac{1}{\sqrt{2}} - \frac{1}{\sqrt{2}}j)$

19. (i) (a) $2j$ (b) -4 (c) $(-4)^k$

Exercise 3C

1–6

7.

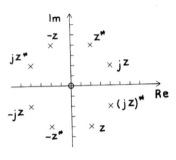

8. Points (i) $10 + 5j$ (ii) $1 + 2j$ (iii) $11 + 7j$ (iv) $9 + 3j$ (v) $-9 - 3j$ (vi) $25j$ (vii) $4 - 3j$ (viii) $\frac{4}{25} + \frac{3}{25}j$

9.

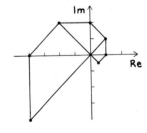

10. Half a turn about O followed by reflection in the x axis is the same as reflection in the x axis followed by half a turn about O.

Exercise 3D

3.

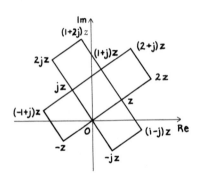

5. $\overrightarrow{AB} = b - a$, $\overrightarrow{DC} = c - d$

6. $2j, -6 + 6j, 4 - 8j$

7. $4 + 7j, -j$

8. (i) $1, 9 - 4j$ (ii) $-1 + 6j, -5 - 2j$ or $15 - 2j, 11 - 10j$

Exercise 3E

1. Circle, centre 0, radius 2.

2. Circle and interior, centre 4, radius 3.

3. Circle, centre $5j$, radius 6.

4. Interior of circle, centre $-3+4j$ radius 5.

5. Circle and exterior, centre $6-j$ radius 2.

6. Point $-2-4j$.

7. Circles, centre $1-j$, radii 2, 3 and the annulus between these.

8.

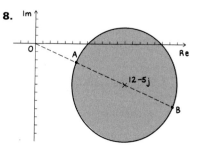

9. 7, 13

10. Not possible.

$|z|$ is least at A and greatest at B.

11. Line $x = 2$.

12. Region $y > 1$.

13. Line $x = -2$.

14. Line $y = x$.

15. Region $y < 5$.

16.

17.

(circumcentre)

18.

Exercise 3F

1. (i) 2 (ii) -4 (iii) $8 + j$ (iv) 0 (v) $-46 - 9j$ (vi) $-46 - 9j$ (vii) $52j$ **2.** $\dfrac{2x}{x^2 + y^2}$ **4.** (ii) $-\frac{1}{2}j$

5. (i) z^*w **6.** (i) $-115 + 236j, -115 - 236j$ (ii) $41^3 = 115^2 + 236^2$ **7.** 0, 2, $-1 \pm \sqrt{3}j$ **10.** (i) $4 - 3j$ (ii) $-4 + 3j$

Exercise 3G

1. $2 - j, -3$ **2.** $7, 4 \pm 2j$ **3.** $p = 4, q = -10$; other roots $1 + j, -6$ **4.** $3 \pm 2j, 2 \pm j$

5. $\pm 3j, 4 \pm \sqrt{5}$ **6.** (i) $(z - 5j)(z + 5j)(z + 3 - j)(z + 3 + j)$ (ii) $U(z) = z^2 + 3z - 5, V(z) = -6z - 15$. (Using the factors in a different order can give different $U(z)$ and $V(z)$.) **7.** $(ac + bd)^2 + (ad - bc)^2$ or $(ac - bd)^2 + (ad + bc)^2$

Exercise 3H

1. $1, 0$ **2.** $2, \pi$ **3.** $3, \pi/2$ **4.** $4, -\pi/2$ **5.** $\sqrt{2} \approx 1.414, \pi/4$ **6.** $\sqrt{50} \approx 7.071, -3\pi/4$ **7.** $2, -\pi/3$ **8.** $12, \pi/6$
9. $6, 3\pi/4$ **10.** $8, \pi/5$ **11.** $0.25, 2.3$ **12.** $3, \pi - 3 \approx 0.142$ **13.** $5, -0.927$ **14.** $13, 2.747$ **15.** $8.062, 1.052$
16. $109.604, -2.128$ **17.** (i) $\alpha - \pi$ (ii) $-\alpha$ (iii) $\pi - \alpha$ (iv) $\frac{\pi}{2} - \alpha$ (v) $\frac{\pi}{2} + \alpha$ **18.** $\cos(-\alpha) + j\sin(-\alpha)$
19. $3[\cos(\frac{\pi}{2} - \alpha) + j\sin(\frac{\pi}{2} - \alpha)]$ **20.** $\cos(\frac{\pi}{2} + \alpha) + j\sin(\frac{\pi}{2} + \alpha)$ **21.** $10[\cos(-\alpha) + j\sin(-\alpha)]$ **22.** $\sec\alpha(\cos\alpha + j\sin\alpha)$
23. (i) Rhombus; $|z| = 2\cos\frac{\theta}{2}$, $\arg z = \frac{\theta}{2}$ (iii) $2\sin\frac{\theta}{2}[\cos(\frac{\theta}{2} - \frac{\pi}{2}) + j\sin(\frac{\theta}{2} - \frac{\pi}{2})]$

Exercise 3I

1.

2.

3.

4.

5.

6.

7. $\pi/3, 2\pi/3$ **8.** $k \leqslant |z + 2k| \leqslant 3k, -\pi/6 \leqslant \arg(z + 2k) \leqslant \pi/6$

9.

10.
11.

12.

Exercise 3J

1. $6(\cos\frac{7\pi}{12} + j\sin\frac{7\pi}{12})$ **2.** $\frac{3}{2}(\cos\frac{\pi}{12} + j\sin\frac{\pi}{12})$ **3.** $\frac{3}{2}[\cos(-\frac{\pi}{12}) + j\sin(-\frac{\pi}{12})]$
4. $\frac{1}{2}[\cos(-\frac{\pi}{4}) + j\sin(-\frac{\pi}{4})]$ **5.** $9(\cos\frac{2\pi}{3} + j\sin\frac{2\pi}{3})$ **6.** $32[\cos(-\frac{3\pi}{4}) + j\sin(-\frac{3\pi}{4})]$
7. $432(\cos 0 + j\sin 0)$ **8.** $10(\cos\frac{3\pi}{4} + j\sin\frac{7\pi}{12})$ **9.** $3\sqrt{2}(\cos\frac{7\pi}{12} + j\sin\frac{7\pi}{12})$ **10.** Exceptions
 (i) if $z = 0$ then $1/z$ does not exist (ii) if z is real and negative then $\arg(1/z) = \arg z$

Exercise 4A

1. (i) $\begin{pmatrix} 3 & 0 \\ 0 & 3 \end{pmatrix}$ (ii) $\begin{pmatrix} 1 & 0 \\ 0 & -1 \end{pmatrix}$ (iii) $\begin{pmatrix} 0 & -1 \\ -1 & 0 \end{pmatrix}$ (iv) $\begin{pmatrix} 0 & 1 \\ -1 & 0 \end{pmatrix}$ (v) $\begin{pmatrix} \frac{1}{2} & 0 \\ 0 & \frac{1}{2} \end{pmatrix}$

2. (a) Reflection in the x axis. (b) Reflection in $y = x$. (c) Two way stretch, $\times 2$ parallel to x axis, $\times 3$ parallel to y axis. (d) Enlargement, $\times 3$, centre O (e) Rotation 45° anticlockwise about O. (f) Rotation through arccos 0.6 anticlockwise about O. (g) Two way stretch, $\times 2$ parallel to x axis, $\times \frac{1}{2}$ parallel to y axis. (h) Shear, with fixed line $x + y = 0$, with e.g. $(0, -1)$ moving to $(1, 0)$. (i) Projection (perpendicularly) onto the x axis.

3. $(8, 10), (2, 3), (16, 21)$ **4.** (x, x); $\begin{pmatrix} 1 & 0 \\ 1 & 0 \end{pmatrix}$ **5.** Shear with fixed line $x + y = 0$, with

e.g. $(1, 0)$ moving to $(0, 1)$ **6.** (iii) Shear with fixed line $x - 2y = 0$, with e.g. $(1, 0)$

moving to $(3, 1)$ **7.** (a) $\begin{pmatrix} 3 & 0 & 0 \\ 0 & 3 & 0 \\ 0 & 0 & 3 \end{pmatrix}$ (b) $\begin{pmatrix} -1 & 0 & 0 \\ 0 & -1 & 0 \\ 0 & 0 & 1 \end{pmatrix}$ (c) $\begin{pmatrix} 1 & 0 & 0 \\ 0 & 0 & 1 \\ 0 & 1 & 0 \end{pmatrix}$

8. (a) Rotation of three-dimensional space 180° about the x axis.   (b) Reflection of three-dimensional space in the plane $x = y$.   (c) Shear with fixed plane $z = 0$, with e.g. (0, 0, 1) moving to (3, 0, 1).   (d) Forming the two-dimensional 'end elevation' of a three-dimensional object, using a scale of 1 : 100.

Exercise 4B

1. (a) $\begin{pmatrix} 0 & 8 \\ 4 & 9 \end{pmatrix}$ (b) $\begin{pmatrix} 6 & 9 & 12 \\ 15 & 21 & 3 \end{pmatrix}$ (c) Not possible (d) Not possible (e) $\begin{pmatrix} -1 & -3 \\ 4 & 2 \\ 0 & -7 \end{pmatrix}$ (f) $\begin{pmatrix} -7 & 26 \\ 2 & 34 \end{pmatrix}$

(g) Not possible (h) $\begin{pmatrix} 29 & 40 & -5 \\ 29 & 41 & 13 \end{pmatrix}$ (i) $\begin{pmatrix} 31 & 0 \\ 65 & 18 \end{pmatrix}$ (j) $\begin{pmatrix} 26 & 37 & 16 \\ 14 & 21 & 28 \\ -8 & -11 & 2 \end{pmatrix}$ (k) Not possible (l) Not possible

(m) $\begin{pmatrix} 55 & 89 & 3 \\ 4 & 19 & 10 \\ 23 & 54 & 41 \end{pmatrix}$ (n) $\begin{pmatrix} 26 & 32 \\ 5 & -5 \\ 13 & 21 \end{pmatrix}$ (o) $\begin{pmatrix} 28 & -18 \\ 26 & 2 \\ 16 & 25 \end{pmatrix}$ **3.** (AC)F = A(CF) = $\begin{pmatrix} 52 & 225 & 49 \\ 128 & 420 & -24 \end{pmatrix}$

4. (a) $\begin{pmatrix} 0.4 & -0.1 \\ -0.2 & 0.3 \end{pmatrix}$ (b) $\begin{pmatrix} -\frac{5}{29} & \frac{7}{29} \\ \frac{2}{29} & \frac{3}{29} \end{pmatrix}$ (c) $\begin{pmatrix} -7 & 26 \\ 2 & 34 \end{pmatrix}$ (d) $\begin{pmatrix} -\frac{17}{145} & \frac{13}{145} \\ \frac{1}{145} & \frac{7}{290} \end{pmatrix}$. $\mathbf{B}^{-1}\mathbf{A}^{-1}$

5. (a) $\begin{pmatrix} \frac{5}{2} & -\frac{3}{2} \\ -3 & 2 \end{pmatrix}$ (b) $\begin{pmatrix} \frac{1}{12} & -\frac{1}{8} \\ -\frac{1}{6} & -\frac{1}{4} \end{pmatrix}$ (c) $\begin{pmatrix} 1 & -2 \\ -\frac{2}{3} & \frac{5}{3} \end{pmatrix}$ (d) $\begin{pmatrix} 12 & -\frac{9}{2} \\ -4 & 2 \end{pmatrix}$ (e) $\frac{1}{eh - fg}\begin{pmatrix} h & -f \\ -g & e \end{pmatrix}$ provided $eh \neq fg$

6. $k = 2$ or 3 **7.** (ii) Reflection in $y = 2x$ **8.** (i) (3, 1), (1, 1), (−6, −2) (ii) 2:1; 2

9. (iii) $\begin{pmatrix} 5 & 0 \\ 0 & 5 \end{pmatrix}$ (iv) Enlargement, ×5, centre O **10.** (i) $\begin{pmatrix} 2 & -\frac{3}{2} \\ -3 & \frac{5}{2} \end{pmatrix}$ (ii) $\begin{pmatrix} \frac{2}{5} & -\frac{3}{5} \\ -\frac{1}{5} & \frac{4}{5} \end{pmatrix}$

(iii) $\begin{pmatrix} 1.1 & -2.4 \\ -1.7 & 3.8 \end{pmatrix}$ (iv) $\begin{pmatrix} 2.6 & -2.1 \\ -2.8 & 2.3 \end{pmatrix}$ (v) $\begin{pmatrix} 1.1 & -2.1 \\ -1.7 & 3.8 \end{pmatrix}$ (vi) $\begin{pmatrix} 2.6 & -2.1 \\ -2.8 & 2.3 \end{pmatrix}$

$(\mathbf{BA})^{-1} = \mathbf{A}^{-1}\mathbf{B}^{-1}; (\mathbf{AB})^{-1} = \mathbf{B}^{-1}\mathbf{A}^{-1}$ **11.** (i) D = (1 1) (ii) N = $\begin{pmatrix} 1 \\ 1 \\ 1 \\ 1 \\ 1 \end{pmatrix}$ (iii) (25 19)SN

12. M = $\begin{pmatrix} 1 & 1 & 2 & 0 \\ 1 & 0 & 1 & 0 \\ 1 & 1 & 0 & 2 \\ 0 & 0 & 1 & 0 \end{pmatrix}$ $\mathbf{M}^2 = \begin{pmatrix} 4 & 3 & 3 & 4 \\ 2 & 2 & 2 & 2 \\ 2 & 1 & 5 & 0 \\ 1 & 1 & 0 & 2 \end{pmatrix}$ $\mathbf{M}^2$ gives the number of 'two-stage'

routes between the resorts. $\mathbf{M}^3$ gives the number of 'three-stage' routes between

the resorts. **13.** (ii) $\begin{pmatrix} 1 & 0 & 0 \\ 0 & 0 & 1 \\ 0 & 1 & 0 \end{pmatrix}$ (iii) $\begin{pmatrix} 0 & 1 & 0 \\ 0 & 0 & 1 \\ 1 & 0 & 0 \end{pmatrix}$ (iv) $\begin{pmatrix} 0 & 0 & 1 \\ 1 & 0 & 0 \\ 0 & 1 & 0 \end{pmatrix}, \begin{pmatrix} c \\ a \\ b \end{pmatrix}$

(v) $\begin{pmatrix} 1 & 0 & 0 \\ 0 & 1 & 0 \\ 0 & 0 & 1 \end{pmatrix}$ After 6 stages the strands will be in their original order.

14. (i) $\begin{pmatrix} 1 & -R_1 \\ 0 & 1 \end{pmatrix}$ (ii) $\begin{pmatrix} 1 & 0 \\ -\frac{1}{R_2} & 1 \end{pmatrix}$ (iii) BA = $\begin{pmatrix} 1 & -R_1 \\ -\frac{1}{R_2} & 1+\frac{R_1}{R_2} \end{pmatrix}$ (iv) No

Exercise 4C

1. X = $\begin{pmatrix} 1 & 0 \\ 0 & -1 \end{pmatrix}$; J = $\begin{pmatrix} 0 & 1 \\ -1 & 0 \end{pmatrix}$ (i) JX = $\begin{pmatrix} 0 & -1 \\ -1 & 0 \end{pmatrix}$; reflection in $y = -x$

(ii) XJ = $\begin{pmatrix} 0 & 1 \\ 1 & 0 \end{pmatrix}$; reflection $y = x$ **2.** RS = $\begin{pmatrix} 2 & -1 \\ 1 & 3 \end{pmatrix}\begin{pmatrix} 3 & 0 \\ -2 & 4 \end{pmatrix} = \begin{pmatrix} 8 & -4 \\ -3 & 12 \end{pmatrix}$

3. M = $\begin{pmatrix} \cos 2\theta & \sin 2\theta \\ \sin 2\theta & -\cos 2\theta \end{pmatrix}$ **4.** R = $\begin{pmatrix} \cos\alpha & -\sin\alpha \\ \sin\alpha & \cos\alpha \end{pmatrix}$ **6.** (ii) $R_\alpha = \begin{pmatrix} \cos\alpha & -\sin\alpha \\ \sin\alpha & \cos\alpha \end{pmatrix}$;

$R_\beta = \begin{pmatrix} \cos\beta & -\sin\beta \\ \sin\beta & \cos\beta \end{pmatrix}$; $R_\alpha R_\beta = \begin{pmatrix} \cos(\alpha+\beta) & -\sin(\alpha+\beta) \\ \sin(\alpha+\beta) & \cos(\alpha+\beta) \end{pmatrix}$. **7.** (i) R = $\begin{pmatrix} \frac{\sqrt{3}}{2} & -\frac{1}{2} \\ \frac{1}{2} & \frac{\sqrt{3}}{2} \end{pmatrix}$;

M = $\begin{pmatrix} -\frac{1}{2} & \frac{\sqrt{3}}{2} \\ \frac{\sqrt{3}}{2} & \frac{1}{2} \end{pmatrix}$ (ii) MR = $\begin{pmatrix} 0 & 1 \\ 1 & 0 \end{pmatrix}$; reflection in $y = x$ (iii) Reflection in $y = (2 + \sqrt{3})x$

8. $M = \begin{pmatrix} 2 & -\frac{1}{3} \\ 3 & 0 \end{pmatrix}$ **9.** (a) $\begin{pmatrix} \cos 2\alpha & -\sin 2\alpha \\ \sin 2\alpha & \cos 2\alpha \end{pmatrix}$ (b) $\begin{pmatrix} \cos 2\theta & \sin 2\theta \\ \sin 2\theta & -\cos 2\theta \end{pmatrix}$

11. (ii) $\begin{pmatrix} -\frac{1}{\sqrt{2}} & -\frac{1}{\sqrt{2}} \\ \frac{1}{\sqrt{2}} & -\frac{1}{\sqrt{2}} \end{pmatrix}$ (iv) $x - 3y + 10 = 0$

12. (b) (i) $\begin{pmatrix} 18 & -9 & 4 \\ 1 & -7 & 2 \\ -1 & -4 & 1 \end{pmatrix}$ (ii) $\begin{pmatrix} 1 & a+7 & b+7c+4 \\ 0 & 1 & c+2 \\ 0 & 0 & 1 \end{pmatrix}$ (iii) $\begin{pmatrix} 1 & -7 & 10 \\ 0 & 1 & -2 \\ 0 & 0 & 1 \end{pmatrix}$ (iv) $\begin{pmatrix} 1 & 0 & 0 \\ -3 & 1 & 0 \\ -11 & 4 & 1 \end{pmatrix}$

(v) $\begin{pmatrix} 1 & -7 & 10 \\ -3 & 22 & -32 \\ -11 & 81 & -117 \end{pmatrix}$ **13.** (a) (i) $\begin{pmatrix} \frac{1}{\sqrt{5}} & -\frac{2}{\sqrt{5}} \\ \frac{2}{\sqrt{5}} & \frac{1}{\sqrt{5}} \end{pmatrix}$ (ii) $\begin{pmatrix} 5 & 0 \\ 0 & 1 \end{pmatrix}$ (iii) $\begin{pmatrix} \frac{1}{\sqrt{5}} & -\frac{2}{\sqrt{5}} \\ \frac{2}{\sqrt{5}} & \frac{1}{\sqrt{5}} \end{pmatrix}$;

$S = \begin{pmatrix} \frac{9}{5} & \frac{8}{5} \\ \frac{8}{5} & \frac{21}{5} \end{pmatrix}$ (b) One way stretch, $\times \frac{1}{5}$ parallel to the line $y = \frac{1}{2}x$, centre O;

$\begin{pmatrix} \frac{21}{25} & -\frac{8}{25} \\ -\frac{8}{25} & \frac{9}{25} \end{pmatrix}$ **14.** (iii) Enlargement $\times b$, centre O; rotation $90°$ anticlockwise about O;

projection perpendicularly on to the x axis   **15.** (i) $k = -24$; enlargement, $\times -24$, centre O

Exercise 4D

1. (a), (d) and (e) are the only linear transformations listed.   **2.** $(\frac{1}{5}p + \frac{2}{5}q, \frac{2}{5}p + \frac{4}{5}q)$; yes

6. $c = \dfrac{1}{m+n}(n\mathbf{a} + m\mathbf{b})$ **9.** (i) No; translation $\begin{pmatrix} 3 \\ -5 \end{pmatrix}$ (ii) $\begin{pmatrix} x' \\ y' \\ 1 \end{pmatrix} = \begin{pmatrix} 0 & -1 & 3 \\ 1 & 0 & -1 \\ 0 & 0 & 1 \end{pmatrix}\begin{pmatrix} x \\ y \\ 1 \end{pmatrix}$; no

10. $\begin{pmatrix} 4 & 0 & 0 & 0 & 0 \\ 0 & 3 & 0 & 0 & 0 \\ 0 & 0 & 2 & 0 & 0 \\ 0 & 0 & 0 & 1 & 0 \end{pmatrix}$

Exercise 4E

1. (a) 10, non-singular   (b) 0, singular   (c) 0, singular   (d) 7, non-singular

4. $ad = 1$ **5.** $[\frac{3}{8}(3s - t), \frac{1}{8}(3s - t)]$; $\begin{pmatrix} \frac{9}{8} & -\frac{3}{8} \\ \frac{3}{8} & -\frac{1}{8} \end{pmatrix}$ **6.** (iii) $x + 2y = 5$

Exercise 4F

1. A pair of lines intersecting at $(6\frac{1}{2}, -\frac{1}{2})$.   **2.** Inconsistent: distinct parallel lines in two dimensions.   **3.** Coincident lines with infinitely many common points: $(\lambda, 2\lambda - 4)$.   **4.** Inconsistent: distinct parallel lines in two dimensions.   **5.** Inconsistent: planes forming a prism.   **6.** A sheaf of planes with a common line: $(2\lambda + 1, 4\lambda + 1, -3\lambda + 5)$.   **7.** Three planes with unique common point: $(3, -14, 8)$ **8.** Three planes with a unique common point: $(-15, 24, -1)$ **9.** Three coincident planes: $(\lambda, \mu, 2\lambda + \mu - 5)$.   **10.** Inconsistent: planes forming a prism.   **11.** $k = 4$: $(\frac{3}{2} - 2\lambda, \lambda)$; $k = -4$: no solution.   **12.** If p and q are not both zero we have *either* no solution (distinct parallel lines) *or* many solutions (coincident lines).   **13.** (i) Inconsistent: planes form a prism   (ii) $(\lambda - 2, \lambda, 2\lambda)$: planes form a sheaf   **14.** It makes no difference whether $\mathbf{A}$ is singular or non-singular.   **15.** 14

Exercise 4G

1. $(\lambda, -\lambda)$ **2.** $(0, 0)$ **3.** $(2\lambda, \lambda)$ **4.** $(0, 0)$ **5.** $y = 2x$; $y = -\frac{1}{2}x$ **6.** $y = -2x$; $x = 0$ **7.** $3y = 4x$; $4y = -3x$

8. $y = 2x$; $y = -2x$ **9.** $y = x$; $y = x + c$ **10.** $x = k$; $y = \frac{1}{3}x + c$; $y = -3x$

11. $y = x$; $y = -x + c$ **12.** None   **13.** (i) -1 or 3   (ii) $(1, -1)$ maps to $(1, -1)$; $(1, 3)$ maps to $(13, 39)$ **15.** (i) 0

(ii) $m = 1, k = 0$; $m = 3, k = -2$; $y = 3x$, $y = x$ (degenerately)   (iii) $y = x$ maps to $(0, 0)$; $y = x + 1$ maps to $(-1, -3)$; $y = x - 2$ maps to $(2, 6)$ (iv) All points on $y = x - 3$ **16.** (i) $(\lambda, 2\lambda)$; $y = 2x$ (ii) (c) $a = -2b$

Exercise 5A

1. (a) $\begin{pmatrix} -23 \\ 13 \\ 2 \end{pmatrix}$ (b) $\begin{pmatrix} 37 \\ 41 \\ 19 \end{pmatrix}$ (c) $\begin{pmatrix} -8 \\ 34 \\ 27 \end{pmatrix}$ (d) $21i - 29j + 9k$ **3.** (a) $\begin{pmatrix} 5 \\ 19 \\ -2 \end{pmatrix}$ (b) $\begin{pmatrix} 14 \\ -62 \\ -9 \end{pmatrix}$ (c) $\begin{pmatrix} -3 \\ -2 \\ 3 \end{pmatrix}$ (d) $\begin{pmatrix} -18 \\ 57 \\ 47 \end{pmatrix}$

4. $\begin{pmatrix} \frac{19}{\sqrt{635}} \\ \frac{15}{\sqrt{635}} \\ \frac{-7}{\sqrt{635}} \end{pmatrix}$ **5.** (a) $5x + 4y - 8z = 5$ (b) $24x + y - 29z = 1$ (c) $19x + 40y + 3z = 188$ (d) $30x - 29y - 24z = 86$

6. (i) $\begin{pmatrix} -1 \\ -12 \\ -31 \end{pmatrix}$; $\sqrt{(1106)}$, $\sqrt{(1106/1155)}$ (ii) $7/\sqrt{(1155)}$ (iv) Using $\sin\theta$ does not indicate whether θ is acute or obtuse.

7. The plane containing **a** and **b** also contains **c**. **8. a** $\times$ **b** is perpendicular to **a**

Exercise 5B

1. (a) $\frac{x-3}{15} = \frac{y-1}{27} = \frac{z}{7}$ (b) $x = y + 3 = \frac{z-5}{-4}$ (c) $\frac{x}{16} = \frac{y+1}{15} = \frac{z+1}{13}$ (d) $\frac{x-2}{11} = \frac{y}{4} = \frac{z-4}{21}$

2. (a) $56.5°$ (b) $80.0°$ (c) $24.9°$ (d) $63.5°$ **3.** (a) $x + 2 = y - 3 = -(z - 5)$

(b) $\frac{x-4}{3} = \frac{y+3}{2} = \frac{z-2}{-6}$ **4.** $41x - 19y + 26z = 33$ **5.** $x + 3y - z + 8 = 0$

6. $\frac{x-4}{21} = \frac{y+2}{4} = \frac{z+7}{11}$ **7.** $60x + 11y + 100z = 900$; $60x - 11y - 100z + 300 = 0$;

$\mathbf{r} = \begin{pmatrix} 5 \\ 0 \\ 6 \end{pmatrix} + t \begin{pmatrix} 0 \\ 100 \\ -11 \end{pmatrix}$; $6.3°$ **8.** (i) $x + 3z + 800 = 0$ (ii) Normal is $18.4°$ approx to horizontal

(iii) $14x - 15y + 3450z - 15\,950 = 0$ (iv) $x = 15\lambda$, $y = -1136\lambda - 62\,396.7$, $z = -5\lambda - 266.7$
(v) 62 km (assuming seam is sufficiently extensive) **9.** (a) $(2, -5, 3)$ (b) $(-1, -3, 4)$
(c) $(5, -2, 1)$ **10.** $\pi_4 = \pi_5$ because π_1, π_2, π_3 have a common line. **11.** (ii) (a) π_2 (b) π_1

Exercise 5C

1. (a) $(3, 2, -13)$ (b) $(1, 2, 7)$ (c) Do not meet (d) $(4, -7, 11)$ (e) Do not meet **2.** No
3. $(-2, -6, -1)$; 30 units **4.** 6, 9, $\sqrt{77}$ **5.** $(5\frac{3}{4}, 3\frac{3}{4}, -\frac{1}{2})$ **6.** $(4, 6, -4)$ **8.** (ii) $(3p - 1, -4p - 4, 7p + 5)$,

$(12, 2q, -3q + 2)$ (iii) $\mathbf{r} = \begin{pmatrix} 8 \\ 6 \\ -8 \end{pmatrix} + t \begin{pmatrix} 2 \\ 1 \\ -1 \end{pmatrix}$ (iv) $(-4, 0, -2)$, $(12, 8, -10)$

9. (iii) $(1, -5, 1)$, $(-1, -1, 5)$, $(-1, 5, -1)$, $(1, 1, -5)$, $(-3, -3, -3)$, $(-5, 1, 1)$ **10.** (ii) $\begin{pmatrix} 1 \\ 2 \\ -2 \end{pmatrix}$, $\begin{pmatrix} 22 \\ -1 \\ 10 \end{pmatrix}$

(iii) $22x - y + 10z = 123$ (iv) $(-1, -15, 13)$ (v) $\frac{x+1}{1} = \frac{y+15}{2} = \frac{z-13}{-2}$ (vi) $(8, 3, -5)$; 27 units
11. 41.9 m; $(8, 42, -11)$, $(41, 21, 4)$

Exercise 5D

1. (a) -2; (b) 29; (c) 0; (d) 34; **2.** (c) W, X, Y, Z are coplanar **3.** $(3, 5, 5)$, $(1, 7, 4)$; $\sqrt{117}$ units
4. (iii) and (iv) $24\frac{1}{2}$ units (v) Method (i) involves fewer evaluations of vector products. **5.** Yes.

Index